The Open

C000055779

Block 2
User requirements
and the design brief

Prepared on behalf of the Course Team by Nigel Cross

T211 Design and designing

This publication forms part of an Open University course T211 *Design and designing*. Details of this and other Open University courses can be obtained from the Student Registration and Enquiry Service, The Open University, PO Box 197, Milton Keynes MK7 6BJ, United Kingdom: tel. +44 (0)845 300 60 90, email general-enquiries@open.ac.uk

Alternatively, you may visit the Open University website at http://www.open.ac.uk where you can learn more about the wide range of courses and packs offered at all levels by The Open University.

To purchase a selection of Open University course materials visit http://www.ouw.co.uk, or contact Open University Worldwide, Walton Hall, Milton Keynes MK7 6AA, United Kingdom for a brochure. tel. +44 (0)1908 858793; fax +44 (0)1908 858787; email ouw-customer-services@open.ac.uk

The Open University
Walton Hall, Milton Keynes
MK7 6AA

First published 2004. Second edition 2009.

Copyright © 2009, The Open University

All rights reserved. No part of this publication may be reproduced, stored in a retrieval system, transmitted or utilised in any form or by any means, electronic, mechanical, photocopying, recording or otherwise, without written permission from the publisher or a licence from the Copyright Licensing Agency Ltd. Details of such licences (for reprographic reproduction) may be obtained from the Copyright Licensing Agency Ltd, Saffron House, 6–10 Kirby Street, London EC1N 8TS; website http://www.cla.co.uk/

Open University course materials may also be made available in electronic formats for use by students of the University. All rights, including copyright and related rights and database rights, in electronic course materials and their contents are owned by or licensed to The Open University, or otherwise used by The Open University as permitted by applicable law.

In using electronic course materials and their contents you agree that your use will be solely for the purposes of following an Open University course of study or otherwise as licensed by The Open University or its assigns.

Except as permitted above you undertake not to copy, store in any medium (including electronic storage or use in a website), distribute, transmit or retransmit, broadcast, modify or show in public such electronic materials in whole or in part without the prior written consent of The Open University or in accordance with the Copyright, Designs and Patents Act 1988.

Edited and designed by The Open University.

Printed and bound in the United Kingdom by Charlesworth Press, Wakefield.

ISBN 978 0 7492 1998 7

3.1

Contents

Exercises

Introduction

Block 2 is concerned with an examination of the early stages in the process of designing and the generation of new products. It explores the interrelationships in product design of the evaluation of user and market requirements, new product planning and the definition of product properties necessary for the establishment of the design brief. Innovation in design is contrasted with broader evolutionary development under the influence of market pressures, technological opportunities and environmental concerns.

The block will involve you in techniques for evaluating existing products. To this end, you will take what is called a user trip. As well as looking at successful products you will explore how things don't work and why. You will also be involved in assessing what users want and need in new product designs.

Examples have been selected from common household products and other consumer goods. Successful design is shown to rely on the establishment of accurate and appropriate technical and market specifications and you will use your studies to create design briefs that underpin such specifications. The skills developed include exploring a design problem, setting objectives and developing a design brief.

You will continue to develop your sketching skills with further use of the *Modelling Workbook* and you will be guided through a number of resources on the DVD-ROM. The assignment (TMA 02) brings together your skills and knowledge. It will involve you in product analysis and will examine your understanding of some of the key aspects of the block such as user research, the writing of a specification and product planning.

Aims and learning outcomes

Aims

This block is about the first steps in the origination of new products. It deals with how companies develop ideas and proposals for a new product and how they define the customer for that product.

Towards the end of the block two key documents that launch and guide the design process for a new product are introduced: the design brief and the design specification.

Although many factors influence the planning and development of new products, the main emphasis within the block is on the requirements of the product user. The types of products I shall focus on are mostly everyday, domestic products.

The aims of the 10 sections of the block are, successively:

1   to place the development of new products within the context of producer companies' commercial strategies, and to introduce some of the forces that help to generate new products;

2   to consider how and why products change and evolve through design improvements in both short- and long-term developments;

3   to introduce the role of market research in new product planning;

4   to consider issues of environmental impact related to product planning and design;

5   to raise awareness of weaknesses in product designs, from the perspectives of usability and the variability in user populations, and awareness of opportunities for product design for different populations;

6   to introduce methods for observing and researching how users interact with products;

7   to consider the evaluation of products, and to establish the relationships between the desired attributes and the physical properties of a product;

8   to introduce methods for analysing user requirements and to relate these to the development of product design scenarios for users of new products or services;

9   to outline the requirements and features of a good brief for a new product design;

10 to outline the requirements and features of product design specifications.

There is important additional material on the course DVD; links to this material are inserted at appropriate points in the relevant sections.

Learning outcomes

After studying this block you should have achieved the following learning outcomes.

1 Knowledge and understanding

You should be aware of:

1.1 the role of new product development within the broader context of a company's business strategy;

1.2 factors and issues that influence new product development;

1.3 principles of user-centred designing;

1.4 relationships between product users' personal values and requirements, and the satisfaction of these through particular product attributes and properties.

2 Cognitive (thinking) skills

You should be able to:

2.1 criticise everyday products from a user's point of view, and suggest new ideas and modifications to improve their design;

2.2 suggest and apply appropriate methods for researching and observing how users interact with products;

2.3 develop design scenarios to provide the context for new product opportunities and ideas;

2.4 write a new product design brief;

2.5 write a product design specification for selected attributes of a new product.

3 Key skills

You should be able to:

3.1 apply comparison and evaluation skills, including constructive criticism of everyday products;

3.2 apply observational skills in the context of both your own and others' use of products;

3.3 apply analytical skills in identifying and interpreting user requirements for product design;

3.4 apply communication skills in writing product design briefs and specifications.

4 Practical skills

You should be able to:

4.1 use various modelling techniques to assist in the communication of ideas and the analysis of products.

Study Chart

Section	Main text	Workbook	DVD	Block 2 Supplement
1	Product planning			Study Guide to Block 2
2	Product evolution	Section 4 Section 5	Modelling Workbook activities 7–9 (video sequence)	Computing notes
3	Design for the market		Design Council case studies	Computing notes
4	Design for the environment			
5	Design for the user		RCA Inclusive Design website archive	Computing notes
6	User research		(three video sequences) IDEO: Design for users; Philips: introduction; Philips: people-centred design	Computing notes
7	Consumer choice			
8	Design scenarios		Personas Creating a persona notebook	Computing notes
9	The design brief			
10	Product design specification			

Support notes for TMA 02 appear in the *Block 2 Supplement*. You should refer to these as you prepare to answer TMA 02.

Product planning

In this section I will look at where, why and how products originate in the plans of companies that make and sell consumer products. I shall attempt to place new product development within the context of such companies' business strategies, and to consider some of the forces that help to generate new products.

1.1   Where do new products come from?

If you look around high-street or shopping-mall stores, you cannot help but notice the number and variety of new products on offer. This year's washing machine or dishwasher, stylish furniture, multi-feature telephones, audio systems, DVD players, digital cameras and camcorders, all beckon the shoppers, asking them to take note of the recent developments. Similarly, press and TV advertisements, leaflets and Sunday supplement flyers introduce us to ranges of brand new, innovative products. Where do such new products come from? Why are so many products launched, relaunched, repackaged, redesigned?

product development
process of devising, creating or improving new products

Most of the companies that are the producers of such goods have a continuous programme of product development, within which they seek to maintain and increase their product sales by continually introducing new products as well as improved and updated versions of their existing products. Occasionally, radically new products appear on the market – products of a completely new type or form. Examples of such products have included ballpoint and fibre-tip pens, pocket calculators, motor scooters, personal computers, video cassette players, video cameras and mobile telephones.

As well as these many successes, there are also frequent failures – radically new products that do not become economic successes and soon disappear. Some of these unsuccessful products include videodisc players, digital audio tape recorders and the Sinclair C5 electrically assisted tricycle.

Introducing radically new products is therefore a risky business, and it is not surprising many companies prefer to stick to the safer ground of more gradual product redesign and development. However, the rewards of successful innovation in product design can be substantial, and therefore many companies are attracted or find it necessary to venture into it.

Case study   OXO Good Grips vegetable peeler

As an example of how new products can be developed, let's look at an apparently simple product, the Good Grips vegetable peeler from the American OXO company. This commercially successful product – like other Good Grips products – has won design awards for its appearance, usability, and innovative use of materials.

Sam Farber, a retired businessman with previous experience in the market for kitchen goods, conceived the Good Grips vegetable peeler. His wife had developed arthritis in her hands, and was experiencing difficulty and discomfort with her kitchen utensils. Conventional vegetable peelers looked like those in Figure 1 – ugly as well as uncomfortable – and Mrs Farber was not impressed with available utensils for people with disabilities.

So Sam Farber realised there might be an opportunity to develop new kitchen utensils for people who had difficulty. Not only that, the utensils could be functional, comfortable, and more aesthetically pleasing for all users. This realisation also fitted with the consumer interest in new, so-called designer products in the 1990s, including kitchen products.

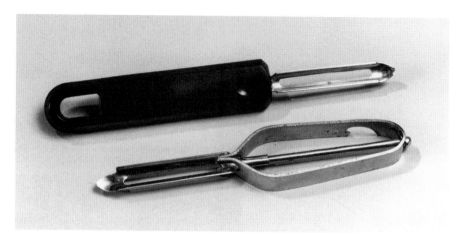

Figure 1 Examples of typical vegetable peelers

So the basic idea was for a new vegetable peeler that would be:

● comfortable and secure to grip and manipulate when dry and when wet;

● usable by, and attractive to, a broad range of users.

Farber decided to invest in developing the product, and took the idea to the Smart Design design consultancy, which carried out research on user requirements, shapes and materials. The consultants developed a design for the peeler handle, based on an oval shape with softer, flexible fins carved into the handle to provide the required improved grip for finger and thumb. They found a neoprene material (Santoprene) that is squeezable and has a comfortable, soft feel with a slight friction to help the grip. The final product design is shown in Figure 2.

Manufacturers in the USA said it was not possible to mould the narrow fins in the neoprene material, but the development team found alternative manufacturers in Japan who were able to produce to the specifications. The resulting high quality of the neoprene moulding has been a significant feature in the product's success. Subsequently, manufacturing transferred to Taiwan where similar quality was established at lower cost.

Figure 2   OXO Good Grips vegetable peeler

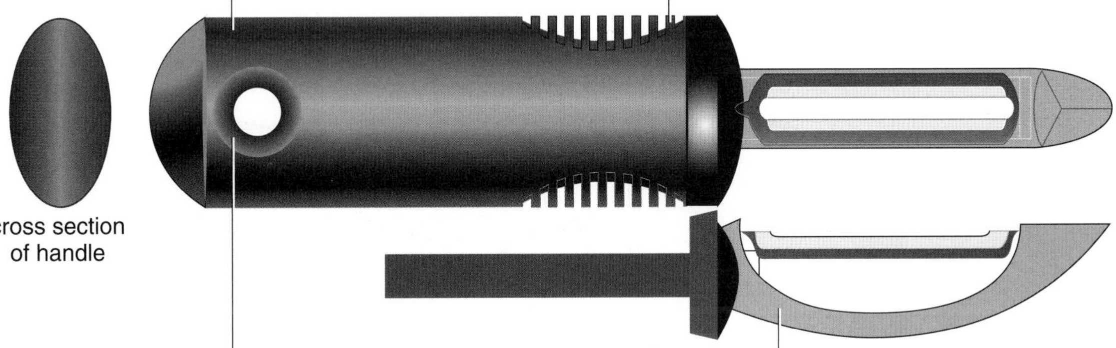

oval handle

- **ergonomics:** optimum shape for hand grip and comfort
- **aesthetics:** oval shape was very popular shape when product was introduced; does not show dirt or oils; blends well with contemporary kitchen environments
- **manufacturing:** shape is easy to mould

fins

- **ergonomics:** allows for comfortable grip with thumb and index fingers
- **aesthetics:** overall shape of curve echoes oval shape of handle; thin parallel fins make handle appear lighter
- **manufacturing:** moulding tolerance of fin thickness challenges structural integrity of Santoprene; thin fins give product a high-quality look that displays dedication to quality manufacturing

cross section
of handle

countersunk hole

- **ergonomics:** allows owner to guide product onto a holder post
- **aesthetics:** the countersunk hole is more subtle than a hole with consistent diameter; the light gives tapered slope an interesting variation of reflection and shadow
- **manufacturing:** the hole reduces amount of Santoprene, reducing cost

shield and core

- **ergonomics:** creates a protective cover over blade
- **aesthetics:** curve echoes shape of the handle
- **manufacturing:** serves as structural core for product; strengthens handle; reduces the amount of metal needed to only the blade; serves as structural support for blade

Figure 3   Details and features of the OXO Good Grips vegetable peeler

Figure 3 shows the details and features of the new peeler design. In their book *Creating Breakthrough Products*, Jon Cagan and Craig Vogel offer the following appraisal of the peeler.

> The peeler has attributes that combine aesthetics, ergonomics, ease of manufacture, and optimum use of materials. Taking full advantage of the surface friction of Santoprene, the handle was press-fit around a plastic core. The core extended out of the handle to form a protective curve over the blade and ended in a sharp point that can remove potato eyes. The plastic guard also serves as the holder for the metal blade (the only metal part left) and the blade is made out of high-grade metal that is sharper and lasts longer than the blades on the older peelers. A final detail was a large countersunk hole carved into the end of the handle to allow owners to hang the peeler on a hook if they preferred. This hole also added an aesthetic detail that offset the large mass of the handle and, along with the fins, gave the product a contemporary look that made it appealing to a much broader audience than originally targeted.

added value
arises from the design and manufacturing processes which give products the attributes and benefits that are valued by potential purchasers

> The overall effect is that of a very sophisticated product with a contemporary look that is superior in every way to its predecessor except for one aspect, the cost. A comparison of the original peeler with the OXO clearly represents where the opportunities for added value were met and exceeded by OXO.

Sam Farber felt that the public would recognise the value designed into the product and would be willing to pay the difference. He had the insight to predict that the public would pay several times the price of the original peeler. He went against the advice of most of his peers. He was right. The social, economic and technical factors were in place and consumers were ready to show their appreciation for a useful, usable, and desirable product and were more than willing to pay the difference. This product won numerous awards and, as a result of the positive praise generated by word of mouth, the product has never been aggressively advertised. As adult children bought the product for their older parents, they found that they liked the product as well. Younger children found it more fun to use and more comfortable to hold. The market swelled and the momentum grew.

(Cagan and Vogel, 2002)

Figure 4   Some utensils from the range of Good Grips products

Since the introduction of the first Good Grips peeler, many other products have been added to the OXO range – some are shown in Figure 4 – and many other producers have taken up the design, manufacturing and marketing principles embodied in the original product.

The Good Grips concept has undoubtedly been a commercial success; but we should perhaps remain slightly sceptical about the good design features it reputedly embodies. For example, it seems the basic concept of an easy-grip handle has been applied as a standard solution – a kind of trademark feature – to a wide range of products that might need different shapes, features and holding positions from the basic peeler. The thin, squashy rib sections in the handle may be comfortable and effective for grip, but what about cleaning them? The design assumes they are to be cleaned in a dishwasher, but will that always be the case?

The OXO Good Grips peeler is not a typical example of new product development because it was conceived and developed by a single entrepreneur.

More usually, new products arise within producer companies, from their deliberate programmes for new product development. But the case study has introduced, in the context of a simple product, a number of concepts and ideas that I will develop later in this block. These include:

- design for usability, design for the user, and inclusive design – the latter means designing for a range of users, such as those with disabilities;

- ideas related to designing for the market, and the concept of market segmentation;
- the added value of design in a product;
- the use of ergonomics in shaping and detailing the product;
- the linking of desired attributes of a product to specifications for its required physical properties.

The case study also introduced concepts that will reappear in later blocks of this course, such as the choice of materials and choosing designs that are suitable for manufacturing.

1.2 Commercial strategy

The Good Grips peeler originated from someone who began to see conventional products from a different point of view, that of a slightly disabled user. He happened to be a business entrepreneur and was able to do something about it.

As you saw in Section 8 of Block 1, nowadays it can be difficult to bring producers and consumers together. Even if it were possible, there is little input that an individual product user or consumer can make to the development of new products. A consumer may very occasionally be involved in some market research, such as responding to a questionnaire or perhaps participating in a new product test, but essentially each individual consumer seems to have little influence on the planning and design of new products. The important decisions are taken by others, and all the consumer can do is to exercise a choice between products at the point of sale.

Collectively, however, consumers are important to producer companies. The mass of consumers, all making their individual purchase decisions, constitute the market for which the companies plan their products so carefully.

The companies therefore engage in market research of various kinds and they respond to the pressures exerted by their more successful competitors in the market. The companies must constantly review and develop their business strategies, of which one of the most important elements is their strategy for new product development.

The situation is shown diagrammatically in Figure 5. The producer's role extends from establishing a business strategy from which new product policies and plans are developed, to designing specific products, then to manufacturing the product. The consumer's rather limited role is to choose and use the available products. The consumer's decisions are, however, influential on future new product development, through the feedback loop of market research.

Figure 5 Roles of producer and consumer

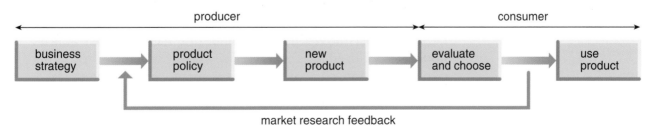

Clearly, this diagram is an inadequate representation of the full set of activities in product planning, specification, design, development, manufacture and sales. The 'new product' box bridges a huge gap in the middle between the producer's product planning options and the consumer's purchase choice. Major sections of the whole product development process lie in this gap.

The producer's product plan will only identify broad ranges or types of products. For instance, a housewares company's product plan might identify the idea of producing a new set of oven-to-table ware, specifically for microwave use. Similarly, a vacuum cleaner company's product plan might identify a need to renew their mid-range model in order to match the price, appearance or performance of their competitors, or a bagless model to meet consumer demand.

From these broad plans, it is necessary to generate some specific product ideas. These ideas might range from improvements to, or redesigns of, existing products, through suggestions for new additions to a product range, to completely new types of products. The ideas might come from the company management, the technical or marketing departments, or design consultants. Given the variety of ideas and potential new products, a screening and selection process is necessary, to reduce the variety down to a smaller number of ideas that can be subjected to feasibility analyses. Eventually, a new product development proposal emerges in the form of a design brief and specification – this stage is described at the end of this block.

In framing their commercial strategy, successful companies tend to consider the question, 'what business are we in?' – not in terms of the products they make but in terms of the market needs they satisfy. This is because the needs that users have tend to be more long-lasting than the products that temporarily satisfy those needs.

A well-known management study many years ago showed usage of the United States railways had declined because of competition from other faster, more convenient forms of transport by road and air. The study suggested that if the railway managers had defined their business in terms of users' transportation requirements, and not just seen their business as railways, they could have integrated with, and extended into other forms of transport.

The idea applies quite generally, as can be seen in a comment from the Gillette company about the previous reliance on aerosol deodorants, after public concerns emerged about damage to the ozone layer from aerosol propellant gases. A Gillette executive said:

> We were like the railroads that didn't realise they were in the transport business, because 80 per cent of all deodorant users preferred aerosols and we were the leader in that segment. But when the ozone controversy broke, we realised we were really in the underarm business.

In other words, the company had implicitly regarded itself as being in the aerosol deodorant market, but when it was forced to reconsider the manufacture of aerosol sprays, it reinterpreted its business mission as 'the underarm business', or personal hygiene products. The identification of the business it is 'really in' is a key part of how a company establishes its business mission and commercial strategy. It has obvious and vital implications for the scope and direction of new product development activity in the company.

SAQ 1

If a deodorant company is 'really in the underarm business', what business would you say the producers of the following products are really in? Think of the needs each product addresses.

(a) vacuum cleaners

(b) computers

(c) potato peelers

(d) televisions

1.3 Technology push and market pull

Many new product developments seem to be based on new technology. For example, pocket calculators, personal computers, mobile telephones and many other new electronics-based products were made possible by the development of the microprocessor chip. There are also many examples of new product development, such as the Good Grips peeler, that do not depend on quite such new technology but on recognising what people want or need – whether that is dishwashers, stacking hi-fi systems, recyclable packaging, and so on. There are therefore two strong aspects to new product development – the push that comes from new technology and the pull of market needs and wants.

These two aspects are usually called *technology push* and *market pull*. Technology itself, of course, does not do any market pushing – that comes from the developers and suppliers of the new technology, and from the makers of the new products. In practice, a lot of new product development is influenced by a combination of both technology push and market pull.

Many companies prefer to work on the market-pull model, using market research to identify customers' wants and needs. The technology-push view, on the other hand, emphasises that applications of new technology can create new demands among consumers and open up new markets. Market research usually cannot identify demands for products that do not yet exist.

A classic case of technology push is that of the original Sony Walkman portable, audio cassette player (Figure 6). No one, not even within Sony, had foreseen that there would be a huge market for such a product – as a non-recording machine audible through headphones, it was thought to have only a limited, specialist market. But it quickly became a successful product innovation that spawned many different versions for different customers (Figure 7) and was copied and adapted by numerous other companies.

Figure 6   Original Sony Walkman (1979)

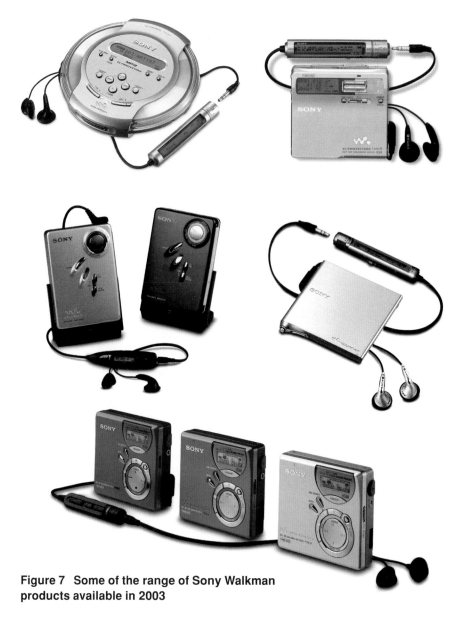

Figure 7   Some of the range of Sony Walkman products available in 2003

Figure 8 shows the matrix of product planning options that face all producer companies. Radical 'product innovation' (top-right sector) occurs when new technology is developed to meet, or create, new markets. But other options lie in the region where an already-developed technology can meet an undeveloped market (top-left sector), and still others lie in the region where new technology can be applied in an already developed market (bottom-right sector). Both of these I've labelled 'product development'.

For example, Sony developed some of its existing products into the new market of children's goods, when it developed its My First Sony products (top-left sector of Figure 8). And it has continually developed (bottom-right sector) new versions of the Walkman concept for its market of teenagers and young adults by taking up new technologies such as CD and MP3 players (Figure 7).

I've labelled the bottom-left sector 'product renewal'. It is where a company's current products lie. In fact, most product design activity occurs within this segment because most companies cannot afford to stand still. There is a constant need for product renewal, through both minor and major product modifications, if the company is to maintain its market position. Companies fail if they cannot renew their products to match those of their competitors.

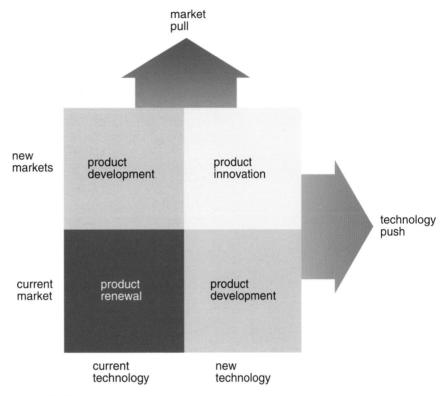

Figure 8   Matrix of opportunity areas for new product planning

SAQ 2

From what you may know about them, try to locate the following products, at the time of their first introduction to the market, within the market-pull-technology-push, product-planning matrix (Figure 8).

(a) Dyson cyclone bagless vacuum cleaner.

(b) Sony Walkman audio cassette player.

(c) Sony Walkman CD player.

(d) IBM personal computer – which established the abbreviation PC.

(e) Any one of a number of low-cost, personal computers launched each year.

Summarise key points of the section

Before you read on, look back over this section and decide what its key points were. In three or four sentences, or with bullet points, write some summary statements in your workfile. Do this before looking at my own summary below, and then compare yours with mine.

Key points of Section 1

New products can arise from a variety of sources, from individual entrepreneurs having a bright idea to companies' strategic plans for extending their markets.

In order to adapt and survive, companies need to set themselves a broad business mission, rather than focusing on specific types of product.

Companies have a limited number of options for new product development areas. Product renewal is the least risky and the most common. Product development is either for new markets or to use new technology. Product innovation is the most risky and radical option, but with potentially large commercial rewards.

Learning outcomes for Section 1 are 1.1 and 1.2

2 Product evolution

As you saw in Section 1, companies rarely rely on creating radical products. The emphasis for most companies lies in maintaining and improving their existing products. Usually this means making minor incremental changes, but sometimes it can also lead to major changes in particular products. This section looks at how some of these changes arise, and at long-term, historical patterns of change and evolution in particular product types.

2.1 Product renewal

We have seen that there are a limited number of strategic options that any company can have for new product development. At the extreme, they can attempt radical product innovation, using new technology to design products for a market need that may not have been recognised before.

Less risky strategies are to seek new markets for modified versions of existing products – perhaps developing versions for younger or older consumers. Companies can apply new technical developments and so create new types of products for their existing market of consumers – for instance by adding new features. The mobile telephone companies have exemplified the latter strategy, with their products becoming smaller, then adding text messaging, e-mail and internet facilities, and then picture taking and sending.

Companies must also seek to maintain their share of the market for their product by continually making modest improvements in the product, in response both to market research and to competition from other companies. These improvements may range from minor changes made to the controls, colours, body mouldings or motors, to major changes that amount to a completely new version of the product.

Case study Frister & Rossman sewing machine

This is a study of product renewal – an example of how a manufacturer of a domestic product, sewing machines, called upon the skills of a designer to revamp one of its products. The aim was to keep its product looking fresh, in order to maintain the product's market position.

The product designer Kenneth Grange was asked by the Maruzen company of Japan to design a new sewing machine for them. Maruzen produces high-quality, well-engineered machines (sold in Europe under the name Frister & Rossman), and were looking for new designs for the European market. The resulting new product design incorporated the standard Maruzen machinery, but repackaged it in novel ways that made it easier to use and gave the overall machine a new and distinctive form and appearance (Figure 9).

Figure 9 Frister & Rossman sewing machine designed by Kenneth Grange

The origins of the new design features lay in Grange's functional approach to design, and on his personal experience. His starting point was his own use of a sewing machine. When I interviewed Grange about the design of the sewing machine, he said:

> I chose to use it, actually making things with a sewing machine, so I did fairly quickly come to understand fundamental strengths and weaknesses.

> (Cross, 2001)

He found a strange 'contradiction' in the sewing machine mechanism being located centrally on its base, when in reality, for most sewing tasks, the user needed more surface area on their side of the needle than behind it. He explained:

> In front of the needle, the longer the table on which you can actually assemble and lay and just get the tension of the fabrics right, the better. Once the work is behind the needle you can do nothing about it, it's sewn.

He therefore proposed moving the sewing machine mechanism rearwards on its base, creating an off-centre layout with more base-table area in front of the needle than behind it. To him, this appeared a virtually self-evident improvement to make.

> This is such a straightforward thing to do, but the reason it had not been done before was because the sewing machine had been designed as a straightforward, basic piece of engineering which needed stability. Therefore the mechanism was from the beginning put centrally upon the base and nobody had thought about challenging the space beyond and the space in front of the needle.

Another radical change in this particular sewing machine design was also a result of a simple, fundamental assessment of how the machine is used. Grange gave the base of the machine rounded lower edges, which look like a mere styling feature, but in fact also arose from function. He explained it like this.

> There was something that they [the company management] told me, which is that a frequent problem with sewing machines, particularly when you are sewing a new fabric, is that a lot of lint comes off the fabric, loose fibres and so on. This gets down into the bobbin and at worst stops the machine, at best it will get itself sewn back into the thing, so you haven't got an absolutely clean stitch, which affects the tension, the thread, etc. And they said, this is a problem, and their way of dealing with it was to make sure you could open the front and get the bobbin out.

This was usually achieved by the user tilting the machine away from them, into a precarious, unstable position that only allowed restricted access to the shuttle mechanism.

To Grange, this was simply inadequate.

> I thought, that doesn't seem to me to be very clever. Why don't we make sure we can open the thing and really get at it? So I tilted the thing sideways, I rolled the whole thing back so it stood up and was very firm, and you could get the whole of the guts apart and get at the lint and so on, and that in itself generated a shape because then the edge of the machine naturally had a roll to it.

The rolled edge made it easier for the user to tilt the machine, it rested stable and secure on its hand wheel, and the underside was accessible for cleaning and oiling the lower mechanisms. A rounded top front edge was also provided to the base plate, to allow the fabric to slide over it more easily, and other features were added such as small drawers for holding accessories. Grange's sketches (Figure 10) help explain these ideas and features.

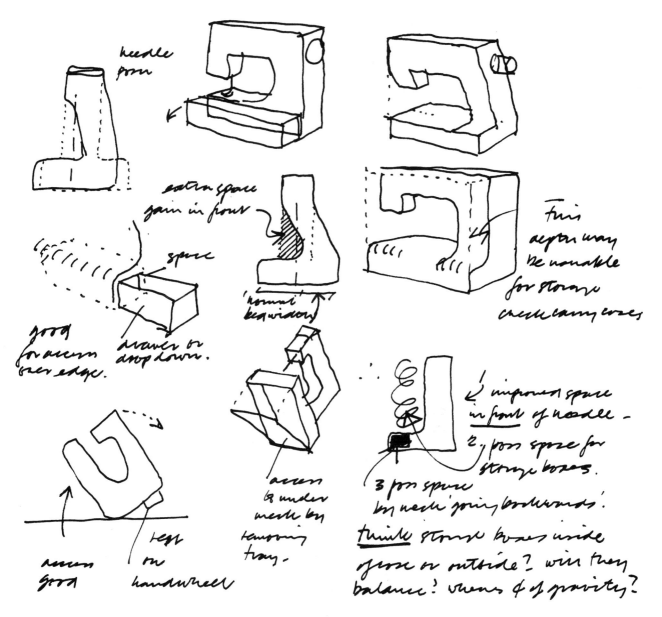

Figure 10 Kenneth Grange's explanatory sketches for the redesign

The sewing machine shows how Kenneth Grange approaches design from the user's viewpoint. The innovative style and features of the new machine were generated from considering and responding to the normal patterns of its use. He said:

> I think it's a question of what your attitude is towards anything, any working thing. My attitude is to want it to be a pleasure to operate.

Another aspect of this approach is that he considers the whole pattern of use. He considered the requirements of periodically cleaning the machine, and considered how the user prepares and introduces the fabric into the stitching mechanism, therefore requiring more make-up space in front of the needle than behind it.

This case study illustrates how a company formed a strategy for product renewal, and then sought ideas for particular products. The Maruzen company called in a designer, expecting some suggestions for styling changes – perhaps changes in shapes or colours. But, like most designers, Kenneth Grange has an attitude of discontent towards most existing products – they can always be improved. In this case, this attitude of constructive discontent meant that Grange looked for ways in which to improve the product from the user's point of view, and was able to generate a new version of a standard product. (This inventive, 'designerly' attitude of constructive discontent will be explored more in Block 3 of this course.) However, no product is immune from being subjected to this attitude, and some have criticised Grange's design for focusing on a limited range of sewing tasks – for example sewing straight seams – and ignoring other more complicated ones.

constructive discontent
a critical attitude of looking at products to spot weaknesses in their designs and find ways of improving them

2.2 Evolutionary forecasting

The design of any particular product type – whether sewing machines, telephones or chairs – will always continue to change and adapt, as long as there is a market for that product type. Sometimes an historical look back over the development of a product type can identify a few major trends or directions of development. Such trends can perhaps be considered as indicators of the evolution of the product.

For example, from their original tall, bulky mass, typewriters gradually became lower, smaller and lighter. In the case of the word-processor the typing surface is a thin keyboard that is completely detached from the display and print functions, and has even been reduced to a foldable, pocket item (Figure 11). During the process of this evolution it might have been possible to forecast the future direction of product development, from an analysis of the past trend.

It is tempting to see such historical product developments as a form of natural improvement – a gradual process of change, something like evolution in nature. However, it is dangerous to draw too close an analogy between natural evolution and this human-induced or artificial evolution. The artificial evolution of products is influenced and determined by technological change, social priorities, marketing pressures, commercial power, consumer habits and, not least, the work of engineering and product designers.

artificial evolution
a supposed historical pattern of gradual change, adaptation and development in product types

The evolution of the typewriter shows that one of the major influences on product development is technological change. This can particularly affect attributes such as speed, power, mass and size. Figure 12 shows how the speed of operation of electric kettles has increased. By projecting the trend forward in time, estimates might be made of when the next significant product introduction might be expected, or of when the current trend might be expected to exhaust itself and a major technological breakthrough be sought. At the time of writing this (2003), one important innovation in a related field has been the growth of microwave ovens – now often used for heating or reheating drinks. Another has been the introduction of specialist drink-making machines in the kitchen such as coffee machines. Could these innovations indicate the beginning of the end for kettles?

(a) Scholes and Glidden, 1875

(b) Remington Standard, 1950

(c) Brother EM-701 electric typewriter, 1986

(d) word-processor keyboard, 1993

(e) Saitek folding keyboard for use with a personal digital assistant, 2002

Figure 11   Evolution of the typewriter

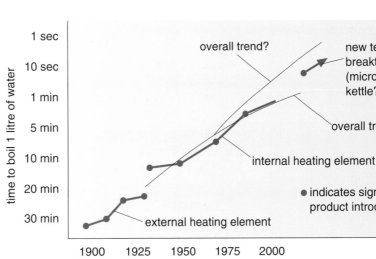

Figure 12   Change in speed of operation of kettles
(Source: Oakley, 1984)

SAQ 3

Thinking back to Section 1.2, what business would you say the producers of kettles are really in?

The technique of *evolutionary forecasting* entails looking at the broad historical development of a general type of product – perhaps the typewriter or the kettle – rather than the details of one specific product. Only major patterns of change are looked for, not small details.

For instance, the evolution of the motor car (European saloon car type) might be categorised as changes to the relative sizes and proportions of the three major spaces provided for people, engine and luggage (Figure 13). Taking 20-year time intervals, the roads in 2020 could be populated by hybrid petrol-electric cars. These would be descendants of the current town car, hatchback and multipurpose models but with adjustments to the spaces for people, engine and luggage.

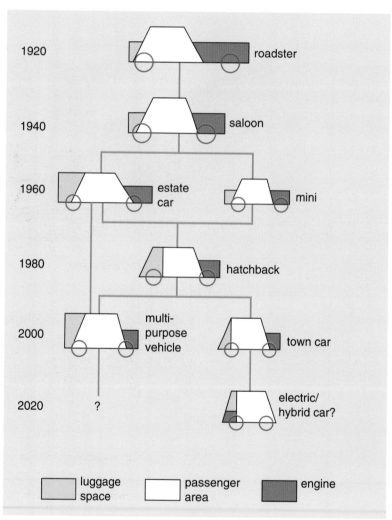

Figure 13   Evolution of the motor car

As a different example, consider the evolution of the domestic cooker (see Figure 14). What were its origins? Domestic cooking used to be done on and around an open hearth, with ovens and water heaters built into the range alongside the fire.

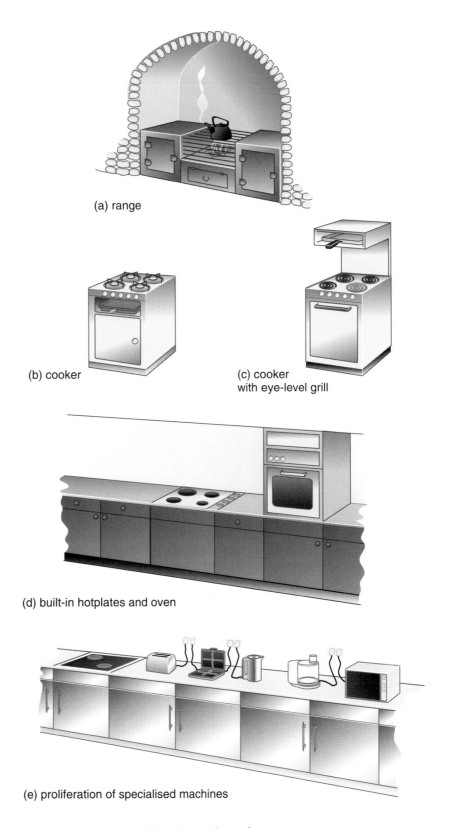

(a) range

(b) cooker

(c) cooker with eye-level grill

(d) built-in hotplates and oven

(e) proliferation of specialised machines

Figure 14 Evolution of the domestic cooker

The first domestic cookers, whether gas or electric, were simple modifications of the range, with oven, grill and hotplate all closely stacked together as though still dependent on the one heat source of the hearth.

A major change in this arrangement was the introduction of the eye-level grill. This took advantage of the possibility with gas and electricity, as opposed to solid fuel, of having different cooking functions separated out and placed more conveniently for the user.

This principle was then adopted more radically, with the hotplates being separated from the oven, and each piece of equipment built-in to the kitchen at the most convenient place.

What has been happening recently is the further proliferation of more specialised food preparation and cooking facilities – toasters, bread makers, microwave ovens, and so on. Cooking and the preparation of meals generally has also changed, often becoming the preparation of a small meal for one or two people, rather than being a meal for all the family, prepared by someone who was usually the cook in the family.

Exercise 1   Future cooking

Save your answers to this and subsequent exercises in your workfile.

From the above analysis of trends in the artificial evolution of domestic cookers, what further changes and product developments might you expect, or could you suggest?

Spend a few minutes on this exercise before reading on.

Discussion

Here are some ideas that I had.

Product proliferation

There are too many new products to be housed in the kitchen, which is usually short of storage and worktop space anyway. Future directions might be towards integration of separate products, such as full-size integrated conventional and microwave ovens, and towards having more of the specialised machines built into the kitchen. What about wall-mounted toasters, built-in kettles or a microwave oven in a drawer?

Hotplate/worktop

There is usually a shortage of worktop space, and hotplates are now built into the worktop, suggesting the two can become one. Some hotplates have a lid that hinges down to cover them and therefore provide a flat work-surface. What about hotplates that hinge up, out of the way, when not in use?

Visible grill

Grill design is often still unsatisfactory – you cannot easily see how the grilling is going without withdrawing the grill pan and/or risking hot fat spitting into your eye. Modern materials have radically altered many features of hotplates and ovens but not grills. Could there be a grill built under the worktop, but with a glass top that allowed you to see the cooking?

Of course, there may be impracticalities in some of my ideas, but assessing trends and making forecasts and conjectures is one way manufacturers plan new product development, and how designers come up with new ideas.

SAQ 4

Summarise the procedure for the evolutionary forecasting method.

Exercise 2   Product evolution

Use the evolutionary forecasting method on some other domestic appliances that have quite a long history, such as the vacuum cleaner, the telephone, the washing machine, and the television set.

This is something that you may have to attempt at various times over a week or so because you may need to consult the Internet, books or magazines, particularly for historical examples, and broad patterns of development may not be apparent at first. Try keeping simple graphic notes of historical examples, and exploring different patterns of evolution.

Summarise key points of the section

Before you read on, look back over this section and decide what its key points were. Write a brief summary of its key points in a couple of sentences, or with bullet points, in your workfile. Do this before looking at my own summary below, and then compare yours with mine.

Key points of Section 2

Many products have evolved over time. Products can become stuck in conventional forms that were established in their origins. Identifying and questioning these can lead to fresh design ideas.

Product types continue to change and develop over time, particularly through influences of technological change, but also in response to a variety of pressures, including changing socio-economic patterns and user requirements.

Learning outcomes for Section 2 are 1.1 and 1.2

Now would be a good time to return to the *Modelling Workbook* to continue your development of drawing skills and knowledge. The *Modelling Workbook* makes two specific contributions to Block 2.

First, Section 4 of the *Modelling Workbook* seeks to develop your basic sketching skills and your ability to present three-dimensional items as a series of related views.

Second, Section 5 of the *Modelling Workbook* takes this a little deeper and introduces another type of 'section', a view that represents the product being cut open for us to see inside.

The learning outcome for the *Modelling Workbook* is 4.1.

3 Design for the market

We have looked briefly at the role of new product development in helping to maintain a company's position in the marketplace. In this section I will review some of the approaches and methods used by companies for identifying and exploiting these marketing opportunities.

3.1 Market research

When Henry Ford launched the Model T in 1909 (Figure 15) he had recognised there was a large unsatisfied demand for motor cars but prices put these beyond the purchasing power of most ordinary people. Accordingly, he set himself the target of making a car to sell for $500, which would bring it within the reach of these people.

To achieve this he designed a standardised product, to be made on a production line, and permitted no variations at all in its specification. This gave rise to the limited colour choice, famously expressed as, 'you can have any colour you want so long as it's black'. By the early 1920s Ford dominated the US car market with over 60 per cent of sales; the Model T still sold for less than $500, a price other producers could not match because they lacked the economies of scale enjoyed by Ford.

However, by 1923 the rival General Motors company recognised that as a result of owning a basic car many users were looking for a more sophisticated product. Accordingly, General Motors developed the concept of a *model range* incorporating different features at different prices – the approach that still dominates mass car manufacture today.

Figure 15   Ford Model T

As a pioneer, Ford offered an undifferentiated product to an undiscriminating customer if for no other reason than that, with no prior experience of it, customers were unable to specify their needs. The product was standardised, and the market of consumers was also assumed to be standardised, so everyone would buy the same product.

3.1.1 Product differentiation

product differentiation
designing different features or characteristics into a product in order to distinguish it from other products of the same type and similar function

market segmentation
dividing the broad market of consumers into subgroups that share certain characteristics or attitudes

With increasing consumer experience and awareness, General Motors saw the opportunity to increase its market share by creating a clear hierarchy of products with different design features – a strategy called product differentiation. The company introduced a range of models aimed at a range of consumers with different requirements, aspirations and spending power. This analysis and subdividing of the market is called market segmentation. When GM did this it displaced Ford as the major supplier within five years.

Figure 16   Some models from the UK Ford range in 2003

The success of the Japanese car producers in penetrating and coming to dominate many world markets in the 1980s was also based on a more developed strategy of researching consumer needs and devising distinctive products to meet particular subgroups or segments of the market. For example, the Mazda company sent a team of researchers and designers to live in California to identify consumer requirements for potential new car models. They spotted trends such as middle-aged men driving old British sports cars at weekends, and younger men buying kit-cars that offered some of the same driving experience at an affordable price.

The team devised the concept of the Mazda MX5 (or Mazda Miata) – a retro-styled, two-seater, open-top sports car, which brought back traditional mechanical features such as rear-wheel drive. But it had all the mechanical reliability and performance aspects that car drivers had come to expect in modern cars (Figure 17). The car became a commercial success with a wider range of consumers than had been envisaged. It continued to evolve through modest product renewal to match changing consumer expectations, and it has had a lasting influence on the whole Mazda range.

If a company has a monopoly, or major control over a market segment, then it can safely produce a standardised product, as Ford did with the Model T and as Sony did with its original Walkman. Other competing companies then have to differentiate their products in some way in order to capture a share of the same market segment.

Figure 17   Mazda MX5 sports car

Such product differentiation may be purely cosmetic such as offering a different range of colour options, but can also extend to performance, convenience and other attributes of the product.

At its simplest, therefore, product differentiation means creating a product that is somehow different from its competitors aimed at the same market segment. However, differentiation of products soon leads into creating products aimed at specific subgroups of the market segment, or at broader or different segments. Manufacturers of consumer products therefore typically offer a product range that has different models for different market segments and that can somehow be claimed or shown to be different from the models offered by competitors. It is market competition, therefore, that drives the proliferation of models for reasons of both product differentiation and market segmentation.

Product differentiation and market segmentation are important aspects of any company's business and marketing strategies. In both cases the company realises that to remain competitive it must cater for the diverse and changing needs of consumers.

3.1.2   Market segmentation

Market segments are groups of consumers identified as having something in common that affects their choice of product. Numerous approaches have been derived for defining market segments, but broadly, they use a variety of factors that are usually grouped into four major categories.

- Geographic – such as country, region, urban or rural, climate.
- Demographic – such as age, gender, family size, income, occupation and ethnicity.
- Psychographic – such as personality, lifestyle, attitudes and hobbies.
- Behaviouristic – such as purchase frequency, usage rate and brand loyalty.

Information about these market segments and their perceived product needs is obtained through market research. Sometimes, the particular language of market research can enter into general usage. A classic case is that of the concept of yuppies, which is a word based on the acronym for young, upwardly mobile, professional people, a key new market segment identified by market researchers in the 1980s.

Example   Up my street

There are many market research companies providing information about market segments, consumer preferences, and so on. They use public information sources such as the national census, as well as their own information gathered from surveys of individuals. Some information is available via the Internet. For example, **upmystreet.com** provides information on neighbourhoods, based on postcodes. Some surprisingly detailed information is provided to upmystreet.com by the CACI marketing data firm, through its ACORN (a classification of residential neighbourhoods) profiles. Here is some of the information provided about the MK7 postcode neighbourhood – around the Open University headquarters in Milton Keynes.

ACORN profile

Type 17: Flats and mortgages, singles and young working couples (0.7 per cent of the population live in this ACORN type).

Likely characteristics

These are affluent areas of single people and couples, living mainly in apartments. The largest concentrations are in London, the Home Counties and central Scotland. They are a feature of relatively prosperous 1980s' boom towns like Slough, Watford and Reading. The proportion of people who have moved home recently is more than double the average.

ITV viewing – *medium*
Ownership of stocks and shares – *medium*
Microwave purchases – *high*
Buying home with a mortgage – *high*
2+ car ownership – *low*
Population aged 0–14 – *low*

Demographics

ACORN type 17 has an interesting age profile. There are slightly above average levels of 0–4 year olds, but only half the national rate of 5–14 year olds. There are above-average levels of 15–24 and 25–44 year olds, but 40 per cent fewer than average people aged over 45. The household structure profile of these neighbourhoods is dominated by single person (non-pensioner) households (2.5 times the national level) and couples without children (33 per cent of households).

Socio-economic profile

Key features of the socio-economic profile are the high levels of working women, above average numbers of clerical and secretarial workers, and well above average proportions of workers travelling to work by rail. These are primarily white-collar areas. The unemployment rate is 30 per cent lower than the national average.

Attitudes

These people budget carefully when shopping. They prefer known brands to own label, and they tend to buy new brands when they see them. They like to take their holidays off the beaten track and would be prepared to pay more for environmentally friendly products. They enjoy radio commercials, but are not particularly receptive to television or press advertisements.

Durables

Car ownership rates are modest, with the majority of households having just one car. Cars tend to be small and cost under £10,000. Company car ownership is 26 per cent above average. Purchase rates on the majority of durables are very low with the exception of microwaves (to cook the large quantities of frozen ready meals consumed here) and space saving washer-dryers that are advantageous in small flats. The proportion of homes installing new central heating is 4.4 times higher than average.

Food and drink

35 per cent more people than average do their grocery shopping on foot. Usage of freezer centres is 19 per cent above average and consumption of frozen ready meals is nearly three times higher than average, though consumption of other frozen foods like beefburgers is very low. Consumption of many packaged grocery products, such as pasta, is very low probably because of small household sizes. Consumption of crisps and snacks, colas and boxed chocolates is well above average. Consumption of fresh foods is low, except sausages.

(ACORN, CACI Limited, 2001 [website: **www.upmystreet.com**])

Exercise 3   Up your street

When you are next on the Internet look up your postcode's ACORN profile on **www.upmystreet.com**. Do you recognise yourself and your neighbours?

Using your own ACORN profile, or the one provided here, identify three bits of information that might be of value to a company producing kitchen electrical appliances.

3.2   Voice of the customer

Product development for lifestyle market segments – such as the Mazda MX5 – is an important feature of Japanese business strategy, and most major product companies will have a department for studying lifestyle, such as Brother's Life Research Centre, and Sharp's Life Soft Centre. The purpose of such centres is to collect information about changes in lifestyle of consumers and to translate customer needs into product functions. A typical example of a study conducted by Sharp's Life Soft Centre was to address the question, 'what kind of people want to use refrigerators – and for what?'.

All over the world, producer companies have increasingly learned to keep a careful watch on emerging consumer requirements and changing user needs and wishes. They have not only learned to listen to what consumers say, but to watch what they do. Techniques used in market research to gather consumers' views on products include both quantitative methods (collecting numerical data), such as survey questionnaires, and qualitative methods (collecting opinions and subjective responses), such as focus groups.

3.2.1 Survey questionnaires

Questionnaires are lists of questions that enable information to be gathered efficiently from a relatively large number of respondents. Most questionnaires require a fixed type of response such as a choice between available answers or along a scale of response. For example, a product design questionnaire might suggest, 'I found the product easy to use' and provide a five-point scale of response from 'agree strongly' to 'disagree strongly'. Or a question might be, 'how often do you use the product?', with responses such as 'every day', 'most days', 'about once a week', 'once every couple of weeks', 'once a month or less'. A realistic and comprehensive range of responses must be available to the respondents – it would be pointless to offer responses to the frequency-of-use question of just 'often' or 'never'.

Sometimes, bipolar scales are used; these offer opposing poles of response, with perhaps a five-point scale spanning between the poles. For example, respondents might be asked to assess a product on bipolar scales such as ugly—pretty, clumsy—elegant, comfortable—uncomfortable, easy—difficult. Advantages of fixed-response types of questionnaires are that they are quick to complete, lend themselves to easy processing of the responses, and result in numerical data.

Another type of questionnaire asks open-ended questions such as, 'are there any features of the product that you dislike?', or, 'would you recommend this product to a friend – if so, why?'. Open-ended questionnaires can provide useful insights gleaned from the responses, or can provide data such as how often a product feature is mentioned in free responses. But they require more processing of the responses, and provide more qualitative feedback and less numerical data than fixed-response questionnaires.

3.2.2 Focus groups

A focus group is simply a group of people gathered together to discuss a particular issue. They have been used in all kinds of social and market research, and by political parties for policy making.

In market research for product design, a focus group might be a group of purchasers of a particular product brought together to discuss the feelings and attitudes towards the product and rival products; or to express the general likes and dislikes about those types of products. The intention of the market researchers is to gather information that might be useful in understanding consumer choices, and provide pointers for product improvements and new product developments.

A focus group would typically have between six to a dozen participants and a discussion leader, in this case the market researcher. The leader will have a list of issues to guide the discussion, but will allow the participants to develop their own topics of discussion, to let the discussion go in directions favoured by the participants. Examples of particular products to be discussed will usually be available.

As group facilitator, the discussion leader tries to ensure that everyone has the opportunity to voice their opinions, and that everyone feels able to raise issues they want to discuss. However, the leader will normally have a set of prompts in case discussion dries up – but it is important that any such prompts are used merely to trigger discussion from the participants, rather than to suggest what those responses might be. Often, this is a matter of phrasing the prompt appropriately. Therefore, for example, rather than asking, 'do you think the material of the handle gives it a high-quality, comfortable feel?', the prompt should be, 'when you hold it, what do you feel about the quality of the handle – and why?'. The leader's aim is to phrase the prompt in a neutral way, like a genuine query, rather than to lead participants into particular responses.

3.3 Products for markets

I mentioned above that Japanese car companies came to dominate in many countries in the 1980s, and this was in part attributable to their marketing research and emphasis on designing products for particular market segments. An example is the car firm Nissan, which researches national preferences for various car attributes in different countries. For instance, it is reputed to have provided its cars with softer suspensions in Germany, firmer steering in the UK, and noisier exhausts in Italy. There are other reasons for the success of Japanese companies, such as their product quality and reliability, but an approach including lifestyle analysis has been used widely by Japanese companies to design products for markets.

For example, the lifestyle design method has been used by the GK-Kyoto company (Figure 18). This method uses lifestyle collages. These are paste-ups of pictures of people, products, situations, and so on, that reflect a particular lifestyle; designers sometimes call these mood boards. GK-Kyoto also uses more formal lifestyle 'maps' of typical life situations, based on contrasting keywords or images of lifestyle.

From these lifestyle maps, characteristic user situations are identified for which there may be new product opportunities. Consideration of these user situations or scenarios, perhaps in creative brainstorming sessions with designers and/or users can lead to product ideas. Images of these potential products in their use situations are then created before finally deciding on a product to develop through to marketing tests.

I will look at scenario development in Sections 8 and 9. Brainstorming and other creativity techniques are introduced in Block 3.

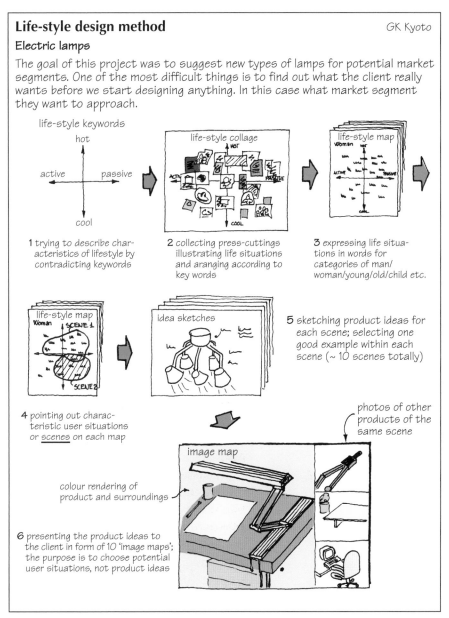

Life-style design method GK Kyoto

Electric lamps

The goal of this project was to suggest new types of lamps for potential market segments. One of the most difficult things is to find out what the client really wants before we start designing anything. In this case what market segment they want to approach.

life-style keywords

hot

active   passive

cool

1 trying to describe characteristics of lifestyle by contradicting keywords

life-style collage

2 collecting press-cuttings illustrating life situations and aranging according to key words

life-style map

3 expressing life situations in words for categories of man/ woman/young/old/child etc.

life-style map

4 pointing out characteristic user situations or <u>scenes</u> on each map

idea sketches

5 sketching product ideas for each scene; selecting one good example within each scene (~ 10 scenes totally)

photos of other products of the same scene

image map

colour rendering of product and surroundings

6 presenting the product ideas to the client in form of 10 'image maps'; the purpose is to choose potential user situations, not product ideas

Figure 18 GK-Kyoto lifestyle design method (Source: Buur, 1989)

3.3.1 Kansei engineering

This kind of designing for the market in Japan has become known as kansei engineering – a phrase adapted from Japanese, which is difficult to translate exactly into English. According to Jordan (2000), kansei engineering translates roughly as 'pleasure engineering' and helps the investigator to understand the relationship between the 'formal properties' and the 'experiential properties' of a product.

Formal properties refer to a product's form – its shape, materials, and so on. Experiential properties refer to the user's experience of the product – how it feels, looks, works, and so on. It can also be used as a means of gaining an insight into the sorts of benefits that people wish to gain from products and the product properties through which these benefits can be delivered.

One approach to kansei engineering involves manipulating individual aspects of a product's formal properties in order to test the effect of the alteration on users' overall response to the product. This technique has been used to assist in the design of a diverse range of products. Examples range from automobiles through camcorders to clothing. Each of several different features of a product – its colour, the shape of a handle, the size of an inset panel, and so on – are varied systematically and separately, and people are asked to make a response to each change, using a fixed-response questionnaire. Statistical analysis of the results indicates which changes, or sets of changes, produce the most favourable responses.

The other approach involves looking at the contexts in which the product is used and then drawing conclusions about the implications of this for the design. This second approach involves the gathering of qualitative data through field observations. In this case, the data is used to help establish the link between the formal properties of a design and the benefits associated with the product.

A kansei engineering approach to camcorder design was based on observing and understanding the context in which people tended to use the product. From looking at marketing data, it was realised that the biggest single user group for camcorders was families who had babies. This meant, for example, that users had to get down on their hands and knees in order to film a baby crawling. To make this easier the researchers recommended a swivelling viewfinder.

Another aspect of use that was noticed was that users would often enjoy showing others what they had just recorded. To do this the users would ask their friends to look through the viewfinder as the tape replayed. To improve on this rather inelegant solution it was proposed to add a monitor screen to the back of the camcorder. This enabled others to watch without having to look through the viewfinder. The combined idea of a swivelling monitor screen is now a normal feature of camcorders.

Similar approaches have been adopted by car manufacturers. In a product renewal exercise for the 2003 model of its Micra, Nissan sent teams of researchers to supermarket and shopping mall car parks to observe how owners of older Micras and similar models stowed their shopping and other paraphernalia. One of the results was to change the design of the Micra's boot to facilitate an owner's needs and habits.

SAQ 5

Compare the kansei engineering approach with the focus group approach.

Summarise key points of the section

Before you read on, look back over this section and decide what its key points were. Write a brief summary of its key points in a couple of sentences, or with bullet points, in your Workfile. Do this before looking at my own summary below, and then compare yours with mine.

Key points of Section 3

Companies use market research to identify different market segments, and provide a range of differentiated products to appeal to different consumers within these market segments. This is market segmentation and product differentiation.

Techniques such as focus groups and surveys are used in market research to capture the voice of the customer. The voice of the customer refers to comments and opinions that influence consumer choice and that need to be taken into account in product planning and design.

Other techniques include analysis of consumer lifestyles or kansei engineering approaches to identify areas for product improvement or suggest opportunities for the development of new products.

Learning outcomes for Section 3 are 1.2 and 2.2

This would be an appropriate point in your study of this block to refer to the case studies of consumer goods design on the course DVD, in the Design Council case studies.

4 Design for the environment

In Block 1 of this course, design for the environment was introduced in the context of chair design. This section develops the theme further, introduces issues of environmental impact related to product design more generally, and considers some of the design responses aimed at reducing or eliminating adverse environmental effects arising from product manufacture, use and disposal.

4.1 Environmental impact

As they work on a product, many designers have to bear in mind the adverse effects on the environment the product and its use may have. In part, this concern has been driven by consumer pressure. Purchasers of products became aware of environmental issues and began to object to disposing of wasteful packaging and learnt about the harmful side effects of product use, such as damage to the ozone layer from the propellant gas in aerosols. In part, concerns also originated with product designers themselves, who became aware of many of the issues before most consumers did.

green design
an attempt to reduce the adverse environmental impacts of a product through tactics such as reducing its energy consumption in use or its toxic emissions on disposal

Designers began to propose green design or eco-design approaches, focusing on using less packaging, eliminating toxic materials, or reducing the energy consumption of products. Some of these approaches led to radically new products.

eco-design
an approach to designing a new product with attention focused on reducing and balancing its environmental impacts over the whole life cycle

The wind-up clockwork radio (Figure 19) was originally developed by the inventor Trevor Bayliss for use in developing countries where batteries and power supplies were not available – his reasons were mainly social rather than environmental. The idea of human-powered radios, and other electronic devices, was later taken up by large companies such as Sony and Philips, because such products appealed to environmentally aware consumers.

(a) Inventor Trevor Bayliss with prototypes of the wind-up radio

Figure 19 Wind-up radios

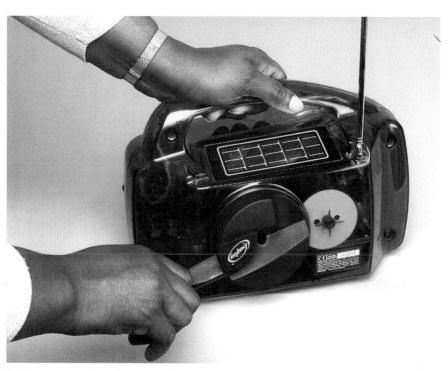

(b) Freeplay radio being wound up

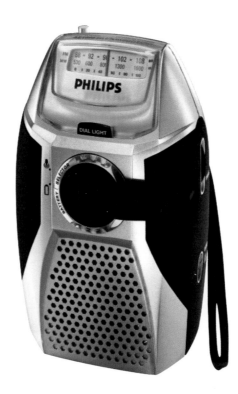

(c) Philips AE1000 wind-up radio

Government legislation has helped to promote environmental awareness among consumers, designers and producers. But the biggest pressure on producers and designers has come from the introduction of government legislation actually banning the use of certain materials and imposing specific standards and requirements for product design, manufacture and disposal. An example is the EU energy labelling of consumer products that requires certain standards of energy efficiency in use (ecolabelling is examined in Block 3). Apart from energy efficiency standards, some of the most significant government legislation in this area requires companies to take back their products when they have come to the end of their life.

The sheer volume and variety of products that are produced in consumer societies has led to a disposal crisis – for example, with refrigerators, car tyres and increasingly with electronic components. The disposal of products at the end of their working life – or at the end of their fashionable use – has therefore become a significant factor in product design. For example, separate components made of different materials have to be designed so that they can be dismantled and recycled.

Some of these aspects of materials choice and manufacturing methods will be dealt with in Block 5 of this course.

For some companies, disposal problems have led them to consider the idea of selling a service rather than a product. This means, for example, that companies lease or hire their products to customers instead of selling them. This type of service is already common with the likes of company cars and office photocopiers. In the extreme, this approach means thinking back to the company's business mission and questioning just what is the service to customers that certain products should provide.

Case study   Kodak single-use camera

A major issue in design for the environment has been the increasing prevalence of disposable products. To use a product just once, or only a few times, and then throw it away suggests the waste of resources and a lack of concern for the environment. However, if a product is returned to its manufacturer after use, rather than being thrown away, then it can probably be recycled quite effectively. As this case study from Cagan and Vogel's *Creating Breakthrough Products* shows, single-use products can, perhaps unexpectedly, exemplify green design.

In the 1980s, prior to the introduction of the single-use camera, photography of events was limited by the necessity of having a camera with you. If you forgot your camera, you missed an opportunity. If you found yourself at an unanticipated event without a camera, then you missed another opportunity. The social, economic and technical factors in an on-the-go world moving into the information age highlighted the need to record on-the-fly experiences through photography.

Kodak understood those factors and in 1987 introduced the single-use camera to meet the needs of customers who wanted an inexpensive camera to take pictures that would have otherwise been missed at various occasions. The first camera was called the Kodak Fling, highlighting its disposable feature – use it and throw it away. However, society was already experiencing a backlash against products that hurt the environment. Soon environmental groups and customers were protesting the sale of the cameras due to their negative effects on the environment. Kodak itself now says the original throwaway was an 'environmental ugly duckling'; yet at the same time the camera was a hit in its intended market.

Kodak found itself in the same position many other companies are in. It had three choices: take it off the market, ignore the protests, or address the concerns. The company chose the third option and around 1991, through a highly integrated effort, totally redesigned the camera to facilitate recycling and reuse of parts.

As the only way to get the film in the camera developed was to take it to a photo finisher, Kodak had a unique opportunity to control the lifecycle of the camera. Once the film is removed, the camera itself is sent to agents to be processed. The camera is designed with minimal variability in materials, and includes recyclable materials wherever possible. All major parts are marked as to their material composition to ease recycling. Although snap fasteners were used to reduce manufacturing time, the number of parts, and variety of materials, the disassembly process at times causes the snaps to break. The agent disassembles the camera and inspects the main polystyrene body. If the main frame is in good shape it is marked to indicate the number of times it was used and sent back to Kodak for reuse. If the part is defective or has been used more than 10 times, it is ground up and recycled. Whenever possible, functions are integrated into a single part to reduce the number of parts used, which also improves tolerance quality. The circuit boards are also tested and, if still functioning well, marked and used up to seven times before being disposed of.

Several parts are only used once to maintain Kodak's high standards as a dependable product. The outer package, made from recycled materials, is again recycled. The lenses are used only once to maintain clarity and then ground up and recycled. The batteries too are only used once to guarantee the flash will function each time. The worn batteries are either used within Kodak for internal pagers or donated to various charitable organisations.

By weight, 77 to 86 per cent of the single-use camera is now recycled or reused. Over 400 million cameras have been recycled rather than thrown in a dump (representing 32 million kilograms of waste diverted from landfills). The only significant difference in value between the re-introduced model and the original Fling is the environmental impact.

(Cagan and Vogel, 2002)

Figure 20   Kodak single-use camera of 2002

4.2 Life-cycle analysis

The problems of environmental impact have highlighted the fact that product planning has to take a complete overview of the life – and death – of a product. This life-cycle approach to product design recognises that environmental issues must be considered in all the stages of product development and design. This starts with the basic product proposal, goes through the design brief and specification, into the choice of materials and detailed design and manufacture; and goes beyond that into use and disposal of the product.

The aim is to identify at which stage of the life cycle the main adverse environmental impacts occur, and to reduce these impacts through design. In other words, the choices open to designers, and the decisions they make, need to be based upon an examination of environmental impact that considers all the life stages of a product. This approach is known as *life-cycle analysis* (LCA).

In general, a satisfactory view of a product's environmental impact can be gained only by examining the range of inputs and outputs throughout the whole life cycle – referred to by some as 'from cradle to grave'. (See Figure 21.) What this simple model seeks to emphasise is that there are likely to be environmental impacts at all stages of the life cycle – mainly air and water emissions and solid waste production, but also including outputs such as heat and noise. Many of these result directly from decisions made by designers, such as in the selection of materials and components.

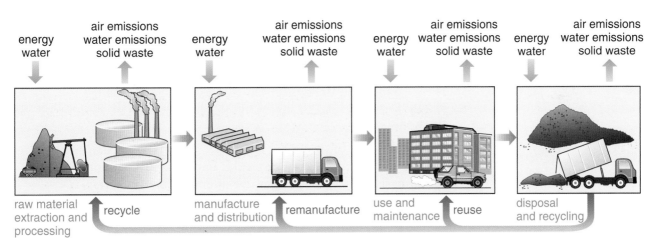

Figure 21 Life-cycle analysis: the main stages in the life cycle of a product, the inputs from and outputs to the environment at each stage, and the possible reuse, remanufacturing and recycling of materials

In part, it is a matter of extending the view of the life of any product back to the cradle – that is, to think back to the stages of raw material extraction and preprocessing into forms suitable for manufacture, because these are often the source of major, perhaps avoidable, environmental impacts. Most obviously, this is evident in the depletion of non-renewable resources such as oil, which might be reduced by greater use of recycled materials or materials from renewable sources.

Where alternative materials or sources are available, they may need to be assessed and selected in terms of comparative environmental impact. For instance, use of raw or semi-finished materials from countries with varying environmental regulations has to allow for the possible presence of toxic residues from different types of processing, not least because subsequent reprocessing may result in inadvertent water or air pollution and, potentially, prosecution.

At the other end of the product's life cycle – the grave – the environmental problems arising from the disposal of materials and components that are not recycled or reused have to be considered. In the life stages between extraction and disposal, it is necessary to take account of any environmental impacts resulting from transporting materials, components and finished products from place to place, as well as from product use and maintenance.

Figure 21 is, of course, a simplified representation, and it understates the potential scale of the environmental impact of a product. For example, the manufacturing and maintenance stages each generate large amounts of non-recycled materials, for instance in faulty and discarded components, and in packaging. Second, non-renewable materials constitute a large part of the discarded materials that end up as waste. Similarly, most of the energy used in the various life-cycle stages is derived from non-renewable fossil fuels such as oil, gas and coal. Third, the interdependences between materials use and energy use need to be kept in mind – choices between materials can have different implications in terms of levels of energy use, whether in production, or in subsequent life stages.

Choosing the materials and components most appropriate for making a product has previously tended to focus on factors directly related to financial and technical performance, such as the costs and availability of materials and the performance characteristics of a component. At the other end of the production process, manufacturers have tended to be concerned with a limited range of post-sale issues, such as cost and performance relative to competing products. These concerns have tended to be limited in duration, and have only occasionally extended across the full life of the product, and rarely into end-of-life disposal.

The importance of designing a product with its performance evaluated in terms of environmental impact across the total life cycle is emphasised by the way that use of energy and materials is distributed across the various stages. For example, it has been known for some time that in the case of a number of energy-using products, such as refrigerators and cars, by far the greatest part of their energy consumption (usually over 90 per cent) occurs in use rather than in manufacture. Whereas for products that don't consume energy in use, such as furniture, the main environmental impacts are usually in materials extraction and processing, and in manufacture. Only detailed cradle-to-grave assessments of different products are able to reveal the full environmental impacts at the various stages.

4.3 Design guidelines

It is important to appreciate that life-cycle analysis is a complex technique and the results of any analysis are dependent on the assumptions built in to each study and the data available. A full assessment of the environmental impacts of complex products, such as cars, with many hundreds of components and designs is difficult. It is usual in such cases to concentrate on the most significant impacts. It is also difficult to make comparative assessments of the impacts of different technical alternatives for achieving the same practical tasks, for example comparing plastics and paper for packaging. In such comparative assessments it is necessary to make judgements about the relative importance of different environmental impacts – for example depletion of a non-renewable resource for plastics production against water pollution resulting from paper manufacture. Life-cycle analysis is therefore a systematic technique that provides vital environmental information to aid decisions on technical and design options, but it is not a simple task and it cannot avoid human judgements and choices.

Faced with the difficulties of preparing a systematic and comprehensive life-cycle analysis for a product, designers and producers therefore look for simpler alternatives, or turn to guidelines that provide advice on general approaches to take towards improving the environmental performance of a product.

There are many different organisations and individuals offering advice on sustainable design. For example, below is a list of qualitative design guidelines based on those published on the website of PRé Consultants in the Netherlands – the company also supplies software tools to aid life-cycle analysis.

Qualitative guidelines for designers

1 Do not design products

Do not design 'green' products but design environmentally sound product life cycles. That is, take into account all processes that occur during the life cycle, from 'cradle to grave', or better, from 'cradle to cradle' (from the beginning of one product life cycle to the beginning of another).

2 Natural materials are not always better

It is commonly believed that 'natural' materials are preferred above 'artificial' or man-made materials. Of course the production of 1 kg of wood causes less emissions than the production of 1 kg of plastic, but have you thought about the paint, the sawing losses? In some products you would need about ten times as much wood as plastic. Plastic can be recycled, wood might not be. Can you really compare on a kilogram basis?

3 Energy consumption is often underestimated

Many designers focus their attention on material selection. This is not always justified. If a product will consume energy in its use, energy consumption should be a dominant consideration in its planning. People normally underestimate the environmental impacts of energy use. These simple examples may help you:

2 kg of oil is required to generate 10 kWh of electricity

1 kg of plastic requires 1.5 to 2.5 kg of oil

A coffee machine uses 300 kWh electricity during its lifetime, equal to 60 kg of oil. During production only 2 kg of plastic is used.

4 Increase product life span

A designer can influence the product life span in several ways. Make it more durable from a technical point of view or make it upgradeable (for example allowing a modern microcontroller to be incorporated in an older computer or washing machine). Try to design the product in such a way people will feel attached to it. Many products are thrown away not because they are broken, but because people get bored with them.

5 Do not design products but services

People do not always want a product. They want a solution for a certain problem. Sometimes a service can be a good solution, like the launderette, instead of many individual washing machines. A good example is also the various car sharing systems currently in use in the Netherlands (and in UK cities such as Milton Keynes).

6 Use a minimum of material

This may seem obvious, but it is more complex than it first appears. Often it is possible to reduce the amount of material by critically looking at dimensions, required strength and production techniques. It can even be beneficial to use materials that have a high environmental load per kilogram, if you can save weight. This is particularly true in transport equipment, where less weight means less fuel consumption.

7 Use recycled materials

Do not only make your product recyclable, but use recycled material in its manufacture. If companies only make products recyclable, there will never be a demand for recycled materials in the future. A sure way to improve the supply of recycled material is to create a demand.

8 Make your product recyclable

Most products could be recycled, but even today very few will be. Only products that are disassembled easily and have a high enough yield will be chosen for recycling. Designers can increase the chance that a product is recycled by optimising its design. The steel part of a car is recycled; the plastic parts are normally not recycled because it is difficult to distinguish, let alone recover, the various plastics that are used. The Volvos made in Holland have a bumper that is made from an unlacquered polypropylene. It is easy to identify, recover and recycle. Televisions can be recycled because the plastic housing contains high grade and therefore expensive plastic. Even the glass from the screen can be recycled. Some plastics, such as thermosetting plastics, have no recycling value. It is better to burn them and reclaim the energy.

(Source: **www.pre.nl/ecodesign/ecodesign.htm**)

4.4 Sustainable strategies

Many companies now perceive design for the environment as a necessary goal. Some embrace the similar but broader concept of *sustainable design*, which addresses social and economic concerns as well as environmental concerns.

This is not only because of government legislation, but also because consumers now expect it. For example, a survey of 600 manufacturers in Sweden, Holland, Germany, France and the UK to explore attitudes and practices towards design for sustainability, conducted on behalf of the UK Design Council in 2001, found the following attitudes among the companies.

- 60 per cent of European companies saw designing for sustainability as an opportunity. Of the 4 per cent of companies who saw designing for sustainability as a threat, most said this was due to prohibitive costs.

- Generally, the larger companies were most active in incorporating design for sustainability. 81 per cent of UK companies interviewed, employing 200+ staff, were producing products incorporating sustainable design principles.

- There were two key influences for companies adopting design for sustainability. Companies in the UK and France emphasise meeting customer demands as the top driver for change, whereas Germany and Sweden strive for competitiveness, suggesting a more proactive attitude to the benefits of design for sustainability. This may be because these latter countries have been forced to deal with regulatory compliance for much longer.

- 87 per cent of all companies believed that design for sustainability had influenced their business strategy.

The majority of companies interviewed saw design for sustainability as an investment, both in terms of future company profits and, more specifically, as an investment for future product development.

SAQ 6

In what ways do you think that concerns with design for the environment would be reflected in a producer company's commercial strategy for new products?

Summarise key points of the section

Before reading my summary of the key points of this section, make your own summary in your Workfile.

Key points of Section 4

Concerns about design for the environment have arisen from adverse environmental impacts generated by the proliferation of products, their use and disposal. But design for the environment is a complex issue, with no simple answers. Even apparently throwaway disposable products can have a substantially reduced environmental impact through take-back, recycling and reuse of materials and components.

A comprehensive approach needs to be based on a cradle-to-grave or life-cycle analysis of a product. The product designer needs to think about raw materials extraction and processing, manufacture and distribution, use, and disposal stages of a product's total life.

A more practical approach can employ simple guidelines for the development of eco-designs.

More radical, sustainable design approaches include not only reducing energy use, increasing product life, and recycling, but also considering social, economic and wider environmental issues. Consideration of the wider context may give rise to radically new ideas for services as well as products.

Learning outcomes for Section 4 are 1.1 and 1.2

5 Design for the user

This section aims to develop your awareness of weaknesses in product designs, from the perspectives of usability and the variability in user populations, and to consider the opportunities for product design for different populations.

Although most producer companies devote major resources to researching the market for their products, many products still appear on the market that seem not to have been designed with the user in mind. Many everyday products can be frustrating in the ways they work – or, rather, *don't* work. These failures can vary from minor irritations, such as the difficulty of using a can-opener; through baffling complications, such as in some computer software; to the downright dangerous, such as poor visibility for the driver in some cars. As modern products become more complex, with more functions available through their electronic controls and displays, many of them have become increasingly confusing to their users. Consequently, a concern has grown to ensure the design of products and systems becomes more user centred.

user centred
user-centred design puts the wants and needs of existing or potential users of a product at the forefront in product development and design

5.1 The frustrations of everyday life

You must have experienced or noticed some dangerous, baffling or irritating product design failures yourself. Perhaps sometimes you thought the failure lay with you, in not understanding how to use the product. Maybe you thought the designers just had not made the product sufficiently idiot-proof – in which case, you were a bigger idiot than the designers had catered for. But wait, you are not alone. Even professors of psychology get baffled by everyday objects. Here is an extract from *The Design of Everyday Things* by Professor Donald Norman.

> If I were placed in the cockpit of a modern jet airliner, my inability to perform gracefully and smoothly would neither surprise nor bother me. But I shouldn't have trouble with doors and switches, water faucets [taps] and stoves. 'Doors?' I can hear the reader saying, 'You have trouble opening doors?' Yes. I push doors that are meant to be pulled, pull doors that should be pushed, and walk into doors that should be slid. Moreover, I see others having the same troubles – unnecessary troubles. There are psychological principles that can be followed to make these things understandable and usable.

> Consider the door. There is not much you can do to a door: you can open it or shut it. Suppose you are in an office building, walking down a corridor. You come to a door. In which direction does it open? Should you pull or push, on the left or the right? Maybe the door slides. If so, in which direction? I have seen doors that slide up into the ceiling. A door poses only two essential questions: In which direction does it move? On which side should one work it? The answers should be given by the design, without any need for words or symbols, certainly without any need for trial and error.

> A friend told me of the time he got trapped in the doorway of a post office in a European city. The entrance was an imposing row of perhaps six glass swinging doors, followed immediately by a second, identical row. That's a standard design: it helps reduce the airflow and thus maintain the indoor temperature of the building.

My friend pushed on the side of one of the leftmost pair of outer doors. It swung inward, and he entered the building. Then before he could get to the next row of doors, he was distracted and turned around for an instant. He didn't realise it at the time, but he had moved slightly to the right. So when he came to the next door and pushed it, nothing happened. 'Hmm,' he thought, 'must be locked'. So he pushed the side of the adjacent door. Nothing. Puzzled, my friend decided to go outside again. He turned around and pushed against the side of a door. Nothing. He pushed the adjacent door. Nothing. The door he had just entered no longer worked. He turned around once more and tried the inside doors again. Nothing. Concern, then mild panic. He was trapped. Just then, a group of people on the other side of the entranceway (to my friend's right) passed easily through both sets of doors. My friend hurried over to follow their path.

How could such a thing happen? A swing door has two sides. One contains the supporting pillar and the hinge, the other is unsupported. To open the door, you must push on the unsupported edge. If you push on the hinge side, nothing happens. In this case, the designer aimed for beauty, not utility. No distracting lines, no visible pillars, no visible hinges. So how can the ordinary user know which side to push on? While distracted, my friend had moved toward the (invisible) supporting pillar, so he was pushing the doors on the hinged side. No wonder nothing happened. Pretty doors. Elegant. Probably won a design prize.

The door story illustrates one of the most important principles of design: visibility. The correct parts must be visible, and they must convey the correct message. With doors that push, the designer must provide signals that naturally indicate where to push. These need not destroy the aesthetics. Put a vertical plate on the side to be pushed, nothing on the other. Or make the supporting pillars visible. The vertical plate and supporting pillars are natural signals, naturally interpreted, without any need to be conscious of them. I call the use of natural signals natural design.

[…]

Devices in the home have developed some related problems: functions and more functions, controls and more controls. I do not think that simple home appliances – stoves, washing machines, audio and television sets – should look like Hollywood's idea of a spaceship control room. They already do, much to the consternation of the consumer who, often as not, has lost (or cannot understand) the instruction manual, so – faced with the bewildering array of controls and displays – simply memorises one or two fixed settings to approximate what is desired. The whole purpose of the design is lost.

[…]

The user needs help. Just the right things have to be visible: to indicate what parts operate and how, to indicate how the user is to interact with the device. Visibility indicates the mapping between intended actions and actual operations. Visibility indicates crucial distinctions – so that you can tell salt and pepper shakers apart, for example. And visibility of the effects of the operations tells you if the lights have turned on properly, if the projection screen has lowered to the correct height, or if the refrigerator temperature is adjusted correctly. It is lack of visibility that makes so many computer-controlled devices so difficult to operate. And it is excess of visibility that makes the gadget-ridden, feature-laden modern audio set or video cassette recorder so intimidating.

(Norman, 1998)

SAQ 7

Outline in your own words, in just one or two sentences, the main design principle that Donald Norman illustrates with his examples in the passage above.

Did you recognise the kinds of problems that Donald Norman experienced? Why do so many everyday objects appear to need a master's degree in technology before you can understand how to use them correctly and easily? Why are so many everyday objects not only difficult to use but actually dangerous?

Many domestic accidents are associated with using everyday objects such as scissors, knives, can-openers and garden tools and machines. These are perhaps inherently dangerous things that need care in their use, but many accidents also result from perfectly normal use of things such as cookers, heaters and even furniture. Of course, many domestic accidents involve young children, or elderly or infirm people; relatively young, healthy adults are less accident-prone. But surely designers realise that not everyone is a young, healthy adult?

Most designers do recognise that often they are designing products for a wide range of users. It is not fair just to blame designers, when they are working to requirements laid down by producer companies and manufacturers, to quality standards set by retail company buyers, and to cost limits set by prices that consumers are prepared to pay.

Exercise 4   How things don't work

Take a look around your home or work environment. Think about the everyday objects you use as you go about your normal activities. Try to look at them with fresh eyes and become aware of shortcomings that you normally take for granted or products that you might blame yourself for not being able to use properly. Note down any problems you notice and try to think of ways in which they might be improved. (Recall from Section 2 the case study of how Kenneth Grange redesigned a sewing machine based on his experience of using it.)

Discussion

Here is my attempt at this exercise.

Having recently installed a new electric hob in my kitchen, I found that I was frequently turning the wrong knob for the hotplate I wanted. The layout of hotplates and control knobs is shown in Figure 22(a). Although each knob has an indicator alongside it of which hotplate it controls, it is still easy to make a mistake unless I consciously search through the indicators to find the right knob before turning it.

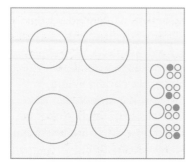

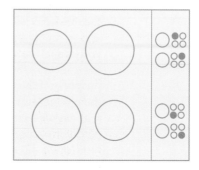

Figure 22

(a) Hotplates and controls on my hob

(b) regrouping the control knobs would make it easier to identify which knob controls which hot plate

There is no obvious way the four knobs in their present position can relate to the four hotplates, so until I have learned from considerable experience it will be necessary to look and choose consciously every time I want to turn on a hotplate. However, I suggest the control knobs could at least have been grouped into two pairs, as in Figure 22(b), so that the relationships could be more obvious.

5.2 Who are the users?

Of course, it is not only me who uses the various products in my home; other people use them as well, both members of the family and visitors. Sometimes the range of users of a product, and their different needs, can be diverse. In addition to the obvious or intended users a variety of people have to interact with the product in various ways at different times, such as the people who make it or service it.

Figure 23 shows a diagram of this. To manufacture the product people have to shape material, drill holes in components, and so on. During assembly, people have to pick up the different pieces and put them together. To be installed, the product has to be transported, fitted into place, connections made, and perhaps performance tested. The product has to be maintained and repaired by people during its working life. Finally, product components are recycled or reprocessed; the different materials have to be separated and this is usually done by hand.

All these stages involve people in one way or another and so, ideally, a full usability evaluation would examine not only how well the product suited the capabilities, limitations and requirements of the user – the product buyer – but all the other people who interact with it as well. For instance, how many times have you tried to repair your car, washing machine or vacuum cleaner, only to find that you do not have the right tool, or the interior parts are inaccessible? These problems are widespread and they do not affect just the amateur at home. Most mechanics or service technicians will tell you stories about designs that make their jobs harder.

Manufacturing requirements can often override even consumer needs. That is because manufacturing and assembly difficulties cost money through lost time, faulty products, accidents and worker dissatisfaction. I had a car once on which it was almost impossible to change one of the spark plugs because it was virtually out of reach behind other components, even when the special flexible plug spanner provided by the manufacturer was used. Of course, it was no trouble to insert the plugs before the distributor, carburettor, air filter, gearshift connector, choke cable and so forth had been bolted on. In other words, the design is compatible with the requirements of one set of users (assemblers) at one stage in the product life cycle but not with the requirements of other users (service mechanics) at a later stage.

The purpose of these examples is to make the point that many designs do not work well in use because the presence of the user is not strongly represented during design. The designer is subject to many, often conflicting pressures that require trade-offs to be made between users' needs and other factors.

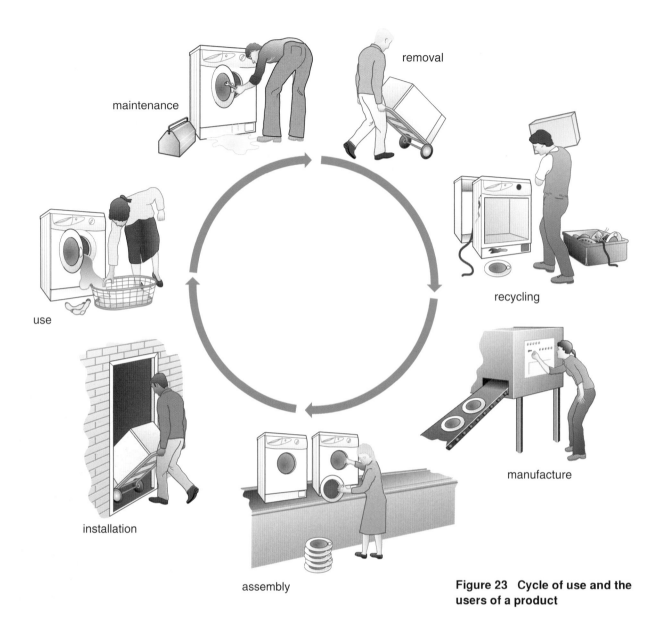

maintenance

removal

recycling

manufacture

use

installation

assembly

Figure 23 Cycle of use and the users of a product

5.3 User populations

Even when user needs are being considered in design, it is still relatively easy for the designer to fall into the trap of designing for some notion of an 'average' user. On the face of it, it seems a good idea to design for the average user. Obviously people do vary but there are limits to variation and surely it should be possible to design for the majority of people.

The problem is that although it is relatively easy, for example, to measure body dimensions of a large group of people and determine what the average values are, it is quite difficult to find individuals who are average in more than just a few of these.

An experiment conducted in the USA illustrates this point (Bailey, 1982). The averages of a large number of physical body dimensions, such as standing height, arm length or chest circumference, are already well known for US adult men. For this study, 4063 males were selected at random and measured to see how well they conformed to the known averages for their population. The first measurement was of standing height and out of the original sample of 4063 only 1055 (25.9 per cent) were found to be average. The rest of the sample was allowed to go home and the experiment continued with only those who were of average height. They were next measured for chest circumference and it was found that only 302 or 7.4 per cent of this group were of both average height and chest measurement. All those not average in both respects were sent home and the experiment continued in this way, working through ten simple dimensions in all. (Figure 24)

By the time the experimenters got to the tenth set of measurements only two subjects were left in the sample and after the tenth measurement even they were eliminated. They had run out of people to measure. No one from the original sample of 4063 subjects was average in all 10 of the dimensions measured. The explanation is of course that every human being is unique, bodily dimensions vary quite widely both in terms of absolute size and in proportion to each other. In other words, the average person is rare, even unique.

original population

average height

average height and weight

average height, weight and hips width

average height, weight, hips width, and knee height

Figure 24 Average person fallacy

Nevertheless it is possible to define populations that have characteristics that are similar to or different from other populations. Generally speaking, adults are taller than children, so age is one criterion we can use to define different user groups. Another is sex: men tend to be taller than women, although some women are of course taller than some men (Figure 25).

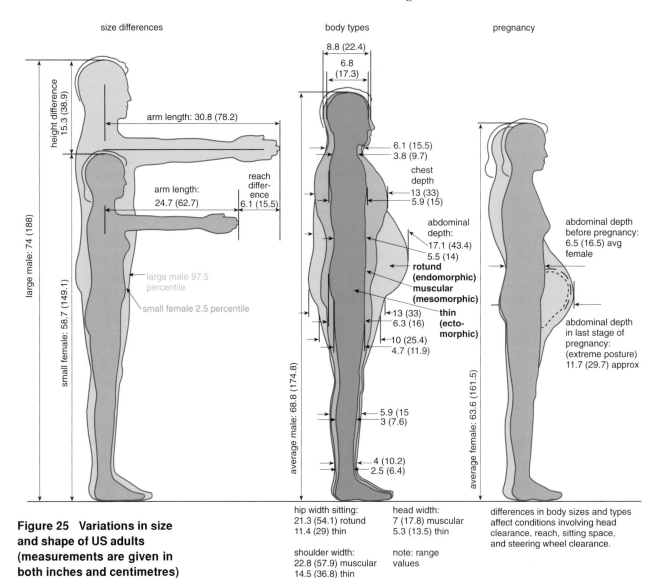

Figure 25   Variations in size and shape of US adults (measurements are given in both inches and centimetres)

Physical condition is another way of looking at variation between different populations. Pregnancy or obesity is a condition that has obvious implications for size and shape. Disabilities that limit movement or that affect physical size and shape may be another way of defining user populations usefully. Factors such as age, size, occupation, leisure interests and personal values may all be relevant characteristics in defining the user population. So instead of thinking about the typical user, a designer needs to keep a representative range of users in mind.

One common way of defining the range of a user population is the so-called method of extremes. Using this method, sample users are selected to represent the extremes of the user population plus one or two intermediate values. In a study to establish recommended kitchen work surface heights, three groups of sample female users were selected for the experiments (see Figure 26).

1   The shortest is around the 2.5th percentile (see below) of the stature range, that is, 1500 mm ± 25 mm.

2   The mean is around the 50th percentile of the stature range, that is, 1625 mm ± 25 mm.

3   The tallest is around the 97.5th percentile of the stature range, that is, 1740 mm ± 25 mm.

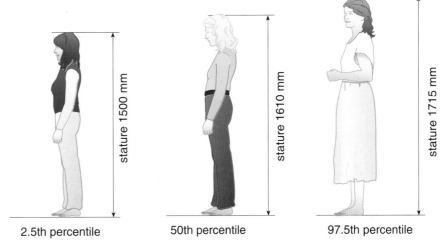

Figure 26   Height requirements for the three groups of people selected for an investigation of the heights of kitchen work surfaces

2.5th percentile   50th percentile   97.5th percentile

The idea of a percentile is quite straightforward. It is that proportion of the population under consideration with a dimension at or less than a given value. So, for example, if the 95th percentile for the standing height of a population is 1795 mm, then 95 per cent of that population are 1795 mm or shorter.

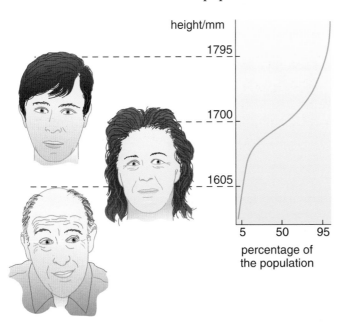

Figure 27   Cumulative graph of heights of a population

This is shown graphically in Figure 27. The horizontal axis shows what percentage of the total population reach a particular height and the vertical axis represents a range of different standing heights. From this figure you can see that 95 per cent of this particular population are 1795 mm or less tall, whereas only 5 per cent are 1605 mm or less, and 50 per cent are 1700 mm or less. Therefore, someone with a standing height of 1605 mm is at the 5th percentile, someone 1700 mm tall is on the 50th percentile and someone 1795 mm tall is at the 95th percentile of this population.

Figure 28 shows the range of body sizes and shapes the product planners considered relevant for the design of a new office chair – the Aeron chair manufactured by the Herman Miller company (Figure 29) that you saw in Block 1. The Aeron chair was designed to fit the smallest and the largest people just as well as it fits imaginary, average people. To achieve this it was designed in three different basic sizes. The A-size chair was designed to fit a 1st-percentile female, with adjustments to accommodate slightly larger people. The C-size chair was designed to fit a 99th-percentile male, with adjustments to accommodate slightly smaller people. The B-size chair was designed around the 50th percentile of users, and adjusts for larger and smaller people. In addition to the adjustable dimensions of the chair components, the material of the seat and backrest is flexible to accommodate differences in body shape. The result, according to the Herman Miller company is that:

> In comparison to a chair designed for the 5th-to-95th percentiles, a 1st-to-99th design fits a surprisingly greater percentage of an actual user population. Applied to a sample of 778 US civilians, a 1st-to-99th design fit 95 per cent of the sample on all four crucial dimensions, compared to the slightly less than 68 per cent that would have been fit by a 5th-to-95th design.

(Source: **www.hermanmiller.com**)

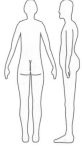 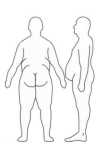 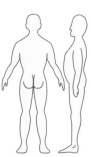 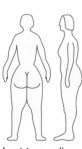 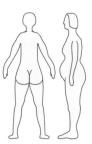 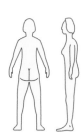

| thin or obese types with clef shaped buttocks | tall, medium or short stocky to obese types | medium to tall, massive upper body, small hip and buttocks types | short to medium, low upper body mass with wide hips, obese buttocks and thick leg | short, medium or tall pregnant female types | short, petite and thin types |

Figure 28 Body shapes and sizes considered in designing the Aeron chair

Figure 29 The Aeron chair

Through focusing on the average user, the producers and designers of products may be overlooking the needs of large sections of the population, as the following analysis by the veteran American designer, Victor Papanek, suggests. As you read the extract from his book *Design for Human Scale*, see if you can spot which of the causes of variation I have described are used by Papanek to expand his target user population.

> For me, it all began with my mother. She was an unusually short woman, about four feet eleven inches [1.5 m] tall. Being so short was quite a handicap. Washing the dishes was enormously difficult for her, since the sink was far too high. Reaching pots, pans, dishes or glasses in kitchen cabinets and on shelves was equally hard. She experienced these same problems when trying to reach goods that had been placed on the upper shelves of grocery stores and supermarkets.

> As far as I was concerned, most of her difficulties arose at home. In 1949, while a design and architecture student, I worked part time in a large New York design office. One evening, finding my boss in a relaxed and rather mellow mood, I told him about some of my mother's problems and asked him if there was anything we as designers could do to help.

He leaned back in his chair, roared with laughter, and said, 'there are more important things for our office to worry about than helping a few little old ladies'.

I went home disturbed. A major difficulty in living and working, which I saw my mother troubled by every day, could apparently not be solved through design. And apart from her, how many other 'little old ladies' were there who suffered from the same problem?

I spoke to my professor who recommended that I make a list. I started with the assumption that my mother was far from unique and that there must be other women four feet eleven inches tall. I did not know where to get hard facts, so I just guessed. If my mother was that short, I estimated that there were probably at least 100 000 other little old ladies in North America. (My guess was wrong: the number was nearly half a million according to the US Census Service for 1940, but I would like the reader to follow the same conservative steps I followed more than thirty years ago.)

If there really were 100 000 little old ladies I guessed there were, it stood to reason that there were also approximately 100 000 little old men.

I now had 200 000 short people. Were there any more?

All of us are between four and five feet tall at some time between our ninth and eighteenth birthdays, and I noted that people in wheelchairs were also shorter than average.

Before looking at the design results, let us analyze what was done. I refused to accept an artificial and narrow definition of the needs of a group considered to be 'too small for concern'. By examining the ways in which this group differed from 'normal' people, I found that these differences were shared by many others.

I broadened the constituency that could be helped through design intervention so much that even a profit-oriented manufacturing and marketing concern would pay attention.

The next step was to see if the same problem, or a similar one, had already been solved at some other time, or in some other culture.

The Japanese, for their own comfort, as well as to keep the tatami floor mats in their homes clean, wear canvas, sock-like slippers called tabi. These tabi separate the big toe from the rest of the foot. When leaving the house, foot and tabi are slipped into wooden thong sandals called geta [Figure 30]. Geta come in many different heights from five to twenty-five centimetres. They keep the feet from touching mud or snow. Obviously, after a heavy snowfall, the tallest geta are worn.

With this information it was possible to develop geta-like footgear that were immediately helpful to my mother [Figure 31]. By developing a clamp-on or step-in device that raised the user's height by nine to twenty-four inches, many chores could be simplified (although made somewhat more precarious). It might be possible to paint the upper parts of walls, paint ceilings, harvest fruit, and do many other tricky jobs that were normally slightly out of reach [see Figure 32].

Having come full circle, I have demonstrated that by broadening the constituency products can be developed that are useful to the remaining 'one-eighth' of humanity.

Another example: most of the world uses straight, lever-action door handles but the United States and Canada are known around the world as the countries with round doorknobs. One minority affected by this

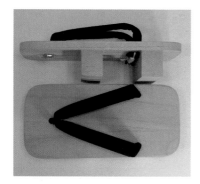

Figure 30   Japanese geta

Figure 31   Drawing of the geta-like elevated slippers designed by Victor Papanek for his mother

practice is the 40 000 myasthenia gravis sufferers who can turn a round doorknob only with great difficulty, due to the weakness of their muscles.

Now to broaden the constituency. Who else has trouble with round doorknobs? Well, there are people with arthritis, the elderly, and small children. There are those who have lost a hand through disease or accident. There are people in wheelchairs and on crutches. There are those who can work a lever with their cane, crutch, hook, stump, or, in the case of quadriplegics, their chin but who have difficulty grasping and turning a round knob. But before this broadening of constituencies becomes a rallying point for the lame, consider this.

All of us have tried to open a door with wet hands after a shower, after coming in from the rain, or after having just done the dishes. And our hands have probably slipped on those silly round knobs. Try visualising a young mother, and small child on her hip, with diapers, bottles, handbag, shopping bag, and keys trying to get in the door. We are all loaded down with packages from time to time and round doorknobs just do not make any sense.

From roughly 40 000 people with myasthenia gravis, I have again broadened our constituency to include nearly everyone.

(Papanek, 1983)

Figure 32   As suggested by Victor Papanek, special stilts have been developed for jobs that require extra height. Here workers wearing stilts install a suspended ceiling

SAQ 8

What causes of variation did Victor Papanek introduce to increase the scope of the user populations he considered?

5.4   Inclusive design

Victor Papanek's approach exemplifies what is now referred to as universal or inclusive design – designing to include everyone. Inclusive design means designing products so that they can be used easily by as many people as wish to do so. This may sound an obvious goal, but the fact is that many people – some estimates suggest as many as one-fifth of all adults – have difficulty carrying out ordinary tasks with everyday products.

Many elderly and disabled people cannot carry out – certainly with any ease or dignity – the range of everyday tasks that others take for granted. They are forced to choose products from a limited range that may suit them, and may have to adapt products themselves, or buy expensive attachments to compensate for a product's inadequate design.

Figure 33 shows a radio with do-it-yourself adaptations made for an elderly user with poor eyesight and arthritis. Some buttons are covered to avoid accidental pressing, which would lose the preset channel, while others have high-visibility stick-on covers. Instructions for retuning the radio presets are attached for carers in case the user does press the wrong buttons. The end of the aerial is padded to avoid accidental eye damage to the user.

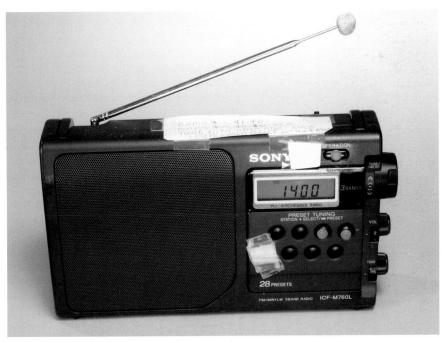

Figure 33   A radio with do-it-yourself adaptations made for a user with poor eyesight and arthritis

Recall from Section 1 that the Good Grips vegetable peeler originated because someone observed the difficulties another person with arthritis had using a conventional peeler. Many producer companies have begun to realise that excluding major sections of the population of potential users of their products is not only unjust but also bad business sense. As the populations in industrialised countries continue to age, there is a growing commercial case for inclusive design. By 2015, nearly 20 per cent of the population of Europe will be aged 65 or over. They will be more active, and have more purchasing power, than previous elderly generations, and will be less tolerant of product designs that 'exclude' them.

Case study   Inclusive power tools

This case study is derived from a research study in inclusive design of power tools for do-it-yourself users. The study was conducted by a research associate at the Helen Hamlyn Research Centre in 2001. This is a centre for research and development in inclusive design at the Royal College of Art in London. The study resulted in new product designs that were marketed by the B&Q do-it-yourself retail company.

DIY is a popular activity – especially among those of retirement age with more time on their hands. But power tools, essential to many basic home improvement tasks, are almost always designed without taking into account the physical impairments that can result from ageing.

As we grow older, our eyesight deteriorates, our strength decreases and our dexterity is reduced. Tools are usually designed for able-bodied workmen and industrial processes – emphasis is placed on purpose rather than ease of use or aesthetics. In particular, power tools are designed for physically strong users, with no attention paid to the growing domestic market of older people.

The challenge was to explore how manufacturers, retailers and designers can be persuaded to take the needs of the older consumer more seriously. Is the answer to produce a range of special-needs equipment or can the needs of older people be successfully written into the design brief of mainstream products?

B&Q is the UK's largest home improvement retailer. Established for over 30 years, the company is known for its wide ranges of products, good value for money and a series of policies ranging from employing older people to serving disabled customers and leading on environmental issues. A key objective for B&Q was to create better designed, own-brand products that fully explore the potential for a design-for-life brand. The company was keen to embody its inclusive attitude within a range of products on sale in its stores.

The research associate first consulted with B&Q to set the project within the company vision. In-store interviews with customers and staff were followed by an extensive product audit supported by desk research and competitor evaluation. From this, key design issues in the area of power tools were identified for further development.

Three different timescales of user testing were used throughout the project. Long-term user testing lasting up to eight months allowed detailed evaluation of existing tools and documentation of issues to be written into the design process. Nine users ranging from a retired carpenter to a businesswoman were selected and given a range of tools and tasks. Users were asked to perform specific DIY tasks with various tools, then informally discuss the process and give feedback on test concepts and prototypes. Focus group meetings lasting about two hours with five older people were conducted during the most intense concept creation stage. Simple product feedback and hands-on prototype evaluation were measured both quantitatively and qualitatively.

There were four design outputs (Figure 34). The cordless screwdriver is one of the most popular power tools yet current tools are long, unwieldy and difficult to grip and activate. A redesign made the shape easier to fit into the palm of the hand and the screwdriver is automatically activated as soon as the screw bit is pushed into the screw.

Cordless drills are heavy to use due to the battery weight. By attaching the battery via a belt clip to the waist and connecting it to the drill with a short power cord, the freedom of cordless drills could be kept while relieving battery weight.

The reciprocating jigsaw has become a best-selling product but little attention has been paid to the ergonomics of holding the saw while applying force. By changing the angle of application and totally redesigning the handle and battery case, a new type of power saw was created.

Figure 34   Power tools designed for the needs of older users: drill, sander, saw, screwdriver

The final concept looked at the popular palm-size sander, which is generally uncomfortable to hold because the user is expected to press and hold it against a surface while it vibrates [...]. The prototype was redesigned to fit the 'cup' of the hand while a hand strap removes the need to firmly grip it.

(Source: **www.designcouncil.info**)

5.5   Ergonomics and human factors

Taking the user as the central point of reference for the design and evaluation of products is the approach encouraged by ergonomists.

The field of ergonomics (also known as human factors engineering) is the systematic study of human capabilities, limitations and requirements, and the application of such knowledge to design. The name comes from the Greek *ergos*, meaning work, and *nomos*, laws. So it means, literally, the laws of work. This title reflects the origins of the approach, which lay in attempts to improve the performance and efficiency of industrial workers and military personnel, through rational, scientific enquiry into human needs and behaviour.

There are two things, therefore, that distinguish ergonomics both from other professional design approaches and from common sense. Firstly, satisfaction of relevant user requirements is the overriding criterion, and secondly, the approach is based on the application of scientific enquiry to the problem of ascertaining human performance, abilities and limitations.

A simple example will illustrate the principles of how ergonomics can be applied in design. Figure 35 shows two designs for pliers. The pair at the top are a familiar conventional design, which appears to make good economic and practical sense. The tool is made in two identical parts, therefore minimising production costs, joined with a pivot. The overall form has evolved over generations from crude forebears such as blacksmiths' tools and acquired a certain elegance and wholeness in its appearance. The design looks as if it has reached an end point in the process of evolution towards a perfect form. The pliers below, on the other hand, look awkward and are made out of two different halves. Yet trials have shown that the ergonomically designed pliers are more comfortable and efficient to use than their traditional predecessors. The reason the conventional design is inferior is because to use it you have to bend your wrist in such a way as to cause unnecessary strain. The ergonomic design is based on studies of the anatomy of the hand, wrist and arm, in particular how the muscles and tendons operate; and the study of how people hold and use pliers.

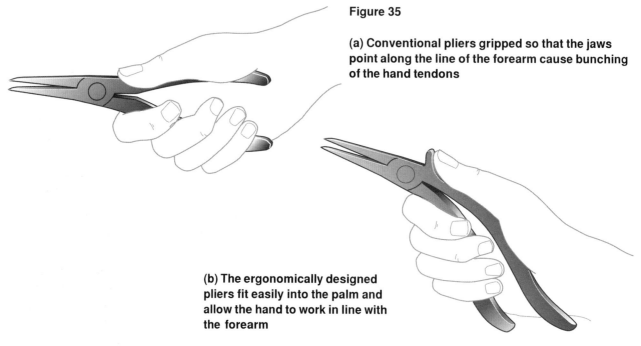

Figure 35

(a) Conventional pliers gripped so that the jaws point along the line of the forearm cause bunching of the hand tendons

(b) The ergonomically designed pliers fit easily into the palm and allow the hand to work in line with the forearm

5.5.1 Displays and controls

A lot of ergonomics research is aimed at establishing guidelines, standards or rules that can be applied by designers in a variety of situations. Where this applies to the physical use of products, much of it is based on standard body measurements. These body measurements are known as anthropometrics.

anthropometrics
the measurement of the dimensions of the human body and its parts; these measurements are used in designing products to match people's needs and capabilities

You have already been introduced to anthropometrics under the subject of 'user populations'. But in performing tasks, many other human factors besides physical height, reach, and so on have to be taken into account by equipment designers. The growth of applications of computers, and the incorporation of computers in products, has meant that interaction design has become a major new area of application for human factors research. Many of us now use information technology devices either directly such as in computer work with word-processing or database applications, or indirectly in products that have embedded computers. We interact with products on a daily basis – from setting a clock-radio or the central heating, to using cash-point machines or buying goods on the Internet – and so interaction design has become a part of the design of most electronic products.

interaction design
design of the sequences and patterns of interactions between a user and a product, especially in respect of computer-based products

Interaction design is concerned with the usability of products and machines, particularly with respect to how they present information to users and respond to commands and inputs from the user.

Recall that a key usability design feature identified by Donald Norman – from his analysis of using everyday objects such as doors – was *visibility*. An everyday object such as a door, or a control such as a button on a product, should appear to be obvious about how it is used, and indeed it should perform that obvious function. For example, is it obvious how you insert a cassette or a disc into a player? Is it obvious how you switch the machine on, adjust volume, and so on?

A second important principle is providing *feedback* to the user. For example, when an action by you has been registered by the machine it may make a click sound, or you hear some other sound or you see something highlighted on a screen.

A third key design feature for usability is *affordance*. This more difficult concept is related to the functions that a product offers, or affords, to its users. Some affordances are real – for example a handle on a portable machine. Some are perceived affordances – these can be more relevant in computerised products, which have more complex and dynamic means of interaction with the user. For these products, it is important for the designer to help the user to perceive just what functions the product affords. Donald Norman defines affordance as:

> Strong clues to the operation of things … When affordances are taken advantage of, the user knows what to do just by looking: no picture, label, or instruction is required.

For many common types of controls on machines, we expect that certain actions, such as turning or sliding them in certain directions, will produce expected kinds of results. Expectations that are found to be widespread in a population are known as conventions or stereotypes. Let's look at an example. Consider the arrangement in Figure 36; which way would you turn the knob to make the pointer on the dial rotate from 1 to 5?

You would almost certainly say clockwise, because the mechanism in Figure 36 takes advantage of two strong conventions. It is normal to expect the pointer to move in the same direction as the knob. Also, people tend to associate clockwise rotation with the actions of on and increase, such as with the volume controls on a radio.

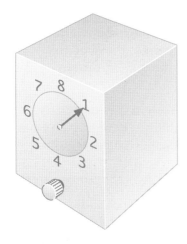

Figure 36 Which way would you turn the knob to move the pointer from 1 to 5?

There are, however, situations in which these conventions are reversed. For instance, in which direction do you turn on a water tap? It is usually anticlockwise, yet I'm sure you don't think every time you turn on a tap that it works in reverse. Generally speaking, the convention is usually anticlockwise for on when dealing with fluids and gases, and clockwise when dealing with mechanical and electrical devices. But there are many variations. For example, a pair of handles on either side of a mixer tap usually turn in contra-directions relative to each other – clockwise and anticlockwise – to turn them on, because it seems more intuitive that both should appear to turn towards or away from yourself to produce the same effect. There are also different cultural conventions – for example, electric switches are flicked down for on in Europe, but up for on in the USA.

intuitive
intuitive use of a product means that how it is used seems natural and obvious and does not need lengthy instruction

Figure 37 Stereotypes illustrating the expected result following the movement of a control

The arrangements in Figure 37 summarise the most common and unambiguous stereotypes for relations between controls and displays.

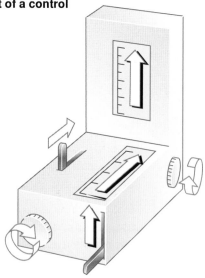

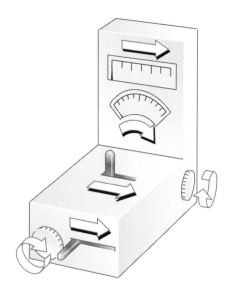

(a) The pointer of the vertical or flat reading instrument would be expected to move in the direction of the arrow in response to the movements shown on the levers or knobs

(b) With horizontal reading instruments the expected display-control relationships are as shown

Stereotypes or conventions can be displaced by alternative learnt responses, but they frequently reassert themselves when tiredness or panic causes stress. Surveys have shown that many errors made by pilots interpreting aircraft instruments result from operating the controls in the wrong direction in response to a visual cue. In another typical example, a hydraulic press was wrecked by its operator. The press was operated by a lever that had to be moved down to raise the ram. One day, when an emergency occurred, the operator panicked and pulled the lever up to raise the ram. It, of course, came down.

The designers of the instrumentation on modern cars pay close attention to stereotypes, conventions, visibility, affordance and our expectations for feedback.

In some situations, therefore, getting a correct design for an interaction with a machine is crucially important. It goes beyond the frustrations of making mistakes in setting your clock-radio. You might like to think about this in relation to the design of the controls on your cooker. (You will recall the difficulties I have with my electric hob controls.) In an emergency, which way would you turn the controls to switch off the heat?

If it is a gas cooker, you turn them clockwise for off, whereas the controls on an electric cooker work the opposite way round. That is because the knobs on a gas cooker are, in fact, taps and it is normal to screw taps clockwise for off. Can you remember the way your bath taps turn?

Electrical controls usually work the other way. The two conventions for gas and electric cookers are so firmly established they cause little trouble on ordinary domestic cookers and would be quite difficult to change. However, mixed gas and electric hobs present a greater potential for confusion.

With increasing use of electronic controls in products, many of the old conventions and stereotypes, based on mechanical devices, no longer apply, and new conventions are being developed. For example, you will probably be used to the idea of pressing and holding down a computer mouse button while the cursor is over a scroll button on the screen to scroll through a document – many computer applications and websites now use this convention, but it is quite a recent innovation. It actually uses a design metaphor from an older technology – the continuous scrolls of texts that preceded printed pages. The use of such metaphors has become fundamental in interaction design, especially in computer systems, which use metaphors of familiar concepts such as desktop, folder or trash can.

However, there is surprisingly little well-established (meaning research-based and observation-based) knowledge about users' expectations and preferences in the field of electronic products. Many designers claim that use of their products is so easy it is intuitive – but there is little evidence of just what kinds and features of electronic controls and displays appear natural or intuitive to users. An example of studying the intuitive use of digital cameras is included at the end of the next section.

Summarise key points of the section

Before reading my summary of the key points of this section, make your own summary in your Workfile.

Key points of Section 5

Many everyday products have annoying failures or weaknesses in their design – some could make the product dangerous. Often, it is not obvious how to use or operate them.

Many different 'users' need to be taken into account in product design.

It can be misleading to design for an average user; a complete user population should be considered, and often it is more relevant to design for an extreme user – for example smallest, tallest, weakest. Designing to include extreme users can also benefit the great majority of users; design should be inclusive where possible.

Knowledge about designing for human capabilities and limitations is derived from ergonomics studies, which can offer general guidelines as well as specific suggestions for good, user-centred product design.

Learning outcomes for Section 5 are 1.3, 1.4, 2.1 and 3.1

This would be an appropriate point in your study of this block to refer to the case studies of inclusive design on the course DVD, in the RCA Inclusive Design website archive.

6 User research

It seems that many aspects of the designed world could be improved. The problems are what aspects and how could they be improved? In this section I am going to look at some common-sense ways of moving from a vague sense of dissatisfaction about a product in general, to more precise criticisms of particular objects. This will involve you in active evaluation tests. So it would be a good idea to plan how you are going to fit these activities in.

6.1 Being a user

I am going to begin by showing you a fairly simple method for structuring the way you approach the evaluation of an object. It is called a user trip and, as its name implies, it requires you actually to go and use the product for yourself and to note down your reactions. Later in this section I am going to ask you to go on a user trip for yourself, but first, here is a description of the method.

6.1.1 User trips

The essential idea of user trips is simple: you just take a 'trip' through the whole process of using a particular product or system, making yourself a critical observant user. Remember how the designer Kenneth Grange began his approach to redesigning the sewing machine by using it and looking for contradictions between the existing product's form and the way it was used.

The only way to learn how to make these user trips is to try one or two for yourself. You will be surprised how much you find out, if you make yourself sufficiently self-aware and observant. In fact, after trying this method a few times, you will probably find that you are adopting an attitude to most of the products and systems used in everyday life, which other people might regard as hypercritical. But it is this critical attitude, this dissatisfaction with the accepted norms, that spurs designers to make improvements. The clever thing is to turn dissatisfaction into constructive, creative criticism.

Decide first which user's point of view you are taking: consumer, operator, maintenance person, and so on. You may want to make several trips, from different user perspectives, or try special user perspectives, such as that of a disabled person. It is usually easiest to take a consumer's trip because you may need special permission, access, and perhaps skills, before you can take any other.

Second, decide the limits and the variations to the user trip or trips you are going to take. It is usually a good idea to extend the trip into activities that both precede and succeed the immediate use of the product you are investigating because this may lead you into devising an improved, more integrated, overall solution. Similarly, variations on a basic trip – different times of day, different weather conditions, different requirements – will probably bring to light a wider range of problems than would a single, random trip.

Third, set out and take the trip and record actions, impressions, ideas and thoughts.

A payphone trip

Let's take as an example using a public (street) payphone. Telephone kiosks are beginning to disappear from our streets, as more and more people have mobile telephones and therefore don't need to use public telephones. But if you have no personal mobile telephone, or it has been lost or stolen, the public telephone kiosk is still a necessity. Perhaps it is time to review its function and role.

So let's consider a public telephone kiosk user trip. What activities would you include in such a user trip, and what variations to a basic trip would you apply? Think about this before reading my suggestions below.

The probable activities are to:

- write down the telephone number on a slip of paper to carry with me;
- check I have loose change; check I have a phonecard and a credit card – either might be needed;
- find and get to a telephone kiosk;
- place the call;
- make any notes.

The possible limits and variations are:

- different times of the day – especially light and dark;
- local and long-distance calls;
- calls to friends and to companies or information services;
- different payphones and payment methods;
- fine and wet weather.

Variations, recording details and being sensitive

The number and extent of the trips and variations that you take will depend on your circumstances and resources, and in which design feature you decide you are principally interested. You could find that one carefully designed trip is adequate for your purposes.

Now you just have to set out and take the trip for real, recording your actions, impressions, ideas and thoughts. Like most people, you may find this strange at first because you have become used to shutting out most of what's happening around you. But on a user trip it is important to be on the lookout for even the tiniest problems or discoveries, because they might add up to something significant. And don't ignore even your most trivial-seeming ideas for improvements, because again they might add up to something bigger, or lead later to an important insight into design faults. This recording of thoughts, impressions, and so on should ideally be done during the trip, or else as soon as possible afterwards. A pocket tape recorder is useful; otherwise use a notebook.

If you are an experienced user of the product or system – perhaps a familiar machine or a regular procedure – remember that you will have adapted yourself to many of the difficulties involved and you will probably be unaware of the impressions that an inexperienced user would have. So try to make yourself again as naïve as you must once have been, and be hypersensitive to even the slightest difficulties or impressions you may have. Alternatively select a situation or trip variation that makes you virtually an inexperienced user, such as using a new piece of equipment or following an unfamiliar routine.

Exercise 5   Take a trip

 Either follow through the example of making a telephone call using a public payphone yourself, or decide on a similar kind of user trip that you can conduct.

Discussion

Below are the notes I made when making a telephone kiosk user trip, taking my own viewpoint, that of an ordinary member of the public.

I decided to telephone some friends, and to check my bank balance by the telephone banking service, on a Saturday in mid-afternoon. The nearest payphone is about ten minutes' walk from my home. I decided to walk, even though the weather did not look promising.

I took a notebook for keeping notes, and wrote the telephone numbers in it. I wrote observations and I had some ideas. I've put some of the ideas in brackets below.

I had to wait while someone else was using the telephone. It began to rain and I got a bit wet. (Idea. Why not incorporate telephones into larger shelters – for example bus shelters?)

While I was waiting I noticed that used phone cards had been thrown away onto the pavement. (Ideas. Design the payphone so it retains exhausted cards. That way litter would be reduced and the used cards could be recycled. Incorporate a litter bin into the kiosk or payphone stand. Convert more payphones for payment by credit or debit cards.)

I wondered how easy it would be to make a call if you were unfamiliar with the process and had difficulty reading the instructions – the case with small children or partially sighted people. (Idea. Have a recorded voice that tells you what to do step-by-step and that gives you feedback if you get into difficulty.)

Some useful numbers, such as emergency services, were displayed in the kiosk, and there were unofficial additions of cards advertising services such as taxis. I also remembered seeing another telephone kiosk that provided internet access, useful for information searching and e-mailing. (Idea. Why not transform the public telephone kiosk into a general-public information service, with touch-screen access to local services and advice, as well as internet access?)

Although my first call was answered, I had got the wrong number because I had mis-pressed a button. This made me wonder about the ease of using the pushbuttons, particularly for people with manual dexterity problems. (Ideas. The use of voice-dialling should be extended, so that the numbers can be spoken rather than pressed. I also wondered about text-messaging; this did not seem possible with the telephone buttons in the kiosk.)

I had to support my notebook on the glass screen to take notes and my pen stopped writing because it was pointing upwards. (Idea. Why not have a sloping shelf with a ledge at the bottom like a writing desk?)

Overall, it was a dull and depressing experience – quite different from the images of telephoning and telemessaging suggested in advertisements by mobile telephone companies. Public telephone services seem in need of radical overhaul if they are to survive. I had begun to develop ideas for telephone kiosks as useful public information services access points.

SAQ 9

Summarise the three main stages in a user trip as described here.

6.1.2 Immersion

A variation on taking just one or a few user trips is to *immerse* yourself in the use of a product over an extended period.

> A more general use of the term immersion to aid creativity will be introduced in Block 3.

The use of immersion to assist the understanding of user needs is described here by the human factors specialist Patrick Jordan in an extract from his book *Designing Pleasurable Products*.

Usually, immersion will involve the investigator experiencing a finished product over a period of time. If, for example the product under investigation were a vacuum cleaner, then the investigator might use this in his or her home. Each time he or she used it, the investigator would record his or her experiences and the opinions that he or she has about the product. He or she might also record his or her impressions when he or she first saw the product and the reactions of others to the product.

If, for example, the product under investigation were a mobile telephone, the investigator might begin by going to an electrical or electronics retailer and looking at the product on the shelf next to other mobile phones. He or she might make observations about how this phone compares with others on display and what his or her reaction to the product was when first seeing it. Would it be the product that he or she would have chosen to buy? If so, why? If not, why not? In what way does his or her reaction to this product differ from his or her reactions to the other phones? Does the design of the phone under evaluation seem more or less sophisticated than the others on display? Does it look like a high-status product or does it look 'cheap and cheerful' or even 'cheap and nasty'? These are examples of the sorts of judgements the investigator may make.

The investigator might then record his or her impressions on first picking up the phone. Examples of the issues to be addressed might include the feel of the phone in the hand – is it pleasant to hold, and does the feeling of the phone radiate an impression of high quality? Do the buttons feel pleasant to the touch? When they are pressed do they give clear and reassuring tactile feedback? Does the phone fit easily into the pocket of the investigator's jacket? Is it comfortable to walk around with it in the pocket?

Next, the investigator might look at some of the usability aspects of the phone. He or she might begin by trying a few basic tasks – making a phone call, receiving a phone call, putting a number into the memory or selecting a number from those stored in the memory. After this, he or she might go 'out and about' with the phone – using it on the street, in the train, in the home, in restaurants and bars or in the workplace. How does he or she feel when using the phone in these situations – embarrassed, proud, important or idiotic? What role does the design of the phone have in affecting the way the investigator feels?

Perhaps the investigator might try using the phone under more 'extreme' circumstances – during a hike in the countryside, or at a football game … Are there any particular aspects of the design of the phone that affect how pleasurable it is in such circumstances? What happens if the phone is dropped? If it is chipped or scratched does this spoil the appearance of the phone, or does it 'wear well' – retaining its appeal despite sustaining wear or damage?

After a period of experience with the phone, the investigator will then make a judgement about how well the phone performs against the criteria by which its pleasurability is to be judged. In the case of a particular phone, for example, these could be as listed below.

> The phone should be guessable. It should be usable at the first or second time of trying for the most basic tasks.

> The phone should be sensorially pleasing in terms of its tactile aspects. It should be pleasant to hold in the hand and buttons on the keypad should feel pleasant to the touch.

> The phone should be a status symbol. The person using the phone should feel that being seen with it enhances his or her status, and others should respond positively when seeing it or when remarking upon it.

> The phone should be easily portable. It should fit nicely into a jacket pocket, handbag or briefcase.

(Jordan, 2000)

Example   Amtrak travel service

Do you remember from Section 1 that someone said the US railroads didn't realise they were in the transport business? Apparently, now they have realised. This study is based on work by the design consultancy firm IDEO for the American railway operator Amtrak, who wanted to create a new design strategy for a high-speed rail link between Boston and Washington. The design research included user trips and immersion techniques. Below are extracts from a report of the research.

Amtrak initially talked to IDEO about product innovation associated with the new service. Amtrak was focused on traditional design and engineering specifications, but IDEO quickly identified that a new passenger experience needed to be designed, not the hardware. As IDEO director David Kelley recalls:

> It was not about, 'how beautiful can we make the train interior?'. It was about competing with the experience of flying or driving by automobile to Washington. It demanded a different way of thinking.

To develop a vision for Amtrak's new service, an IDEO design team based in New York rode Amtrak trains, toured stations, interviewed senior managers, analysed information distribution, evaluated advertising campaigns and probed customer research. They explored different passenger needs through a series of improvised user scenarios, for example buying return tickets from a machine with gloves on or in windy conditions. By analysing the total passenger experience, IDEO identified ten steps: learning, planning, starting, entering, ticketing, waiting, boarding, riding, arriving and continuing.

Each aspect was then developed in relation to the next as part of a seamless experience. The following were sewn into a carefully considered passenger narrative (see Figure 38).

- learning about the Amtrak service via the web or advertising;
- planning an appropriate schedule with timings and fares;
- starting out to the rail station with the right information and route and encountering the right baggage handling and car parking services;
- entering the station with a welcoming infrastructure and environment;
- ensuring the ticketing service was well handled;
- providing platform information, comfort and seating so that waiting is a pleasant drama in anticipation of the train's arrival;
- boarding the train easily;
- riding the train with quality onboard business and leisure amenities;
- providing the right orientation facilities on arrival at the destination;
- planning onward journeys for continuing travellers, for example shuttles to conferences.

Amtrak was presented with a set of recommendations and principles that not only added up to an integrated service in operational terms, but also captured the user-friendly spirit of a quality competitor to the airline shuttles between Boston, New York and Washington. These guidelines extended from naming and branding to new trains and station environments, and signalled IDEO's own departure from its orthodox product development roots into the new terrain of designing entire experiences.

(Source: adapted from Myerson, 2001)

Figure 38 The user's trip scenario developed for Amtrak

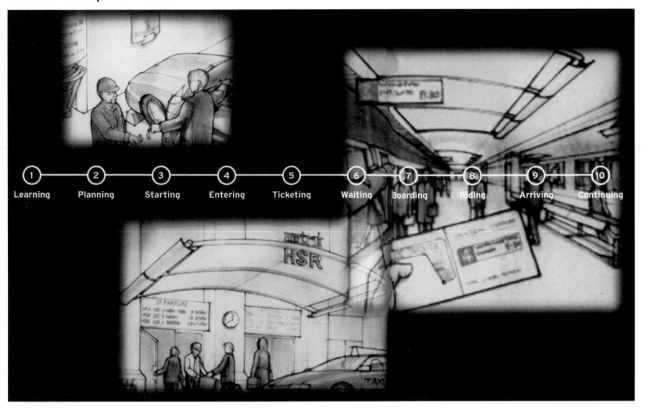

6.2 Observing users

User trips and immersion can generate a surprisingly high number of ideas for improvements to everyday products. This is particularly so if you can adopt a naïve or inexperienced user approach to the product, but this is not always easy. Quite apart from the difficulty of adopting a genuinely naïve approach, user trips and immersion suffer from a number of shortcomings that limit their usefulness.

Can you think of any of these shortcomings?

1 It is often difficult to do something and record your thoughts about it at the same time.

2 As we have seen, a single product can have many different kinds of users and it is often difficult to take the viewpoint of a user who has a role different from your own.

3 A naïve user may make silly mistakes that an experienced user would not, therefore obtaining a wrong impression of the product.

One way around these difficulties is to observe other people acting as users and to choose naïve or different kinds of experienced users, depending on what information you want to gather.

Begin by identifying those experienced users who will be able to provide you with relevant information. Most people are usually willing to cooperate and speak their minds if approached tactfully and with obvious good intent. It is as well to have a short list of questions you want to cover when consulting users, but avoid, for these purposes, a formal, rigorous questionnaire. Stick at first to unstructured discussions with the users, and get them to describe and comment on what seems important to them, as well as on what you regard as important.

Record what you are told, and your impressions of what you are told, during or immediately after the consultation.

As experienced users will have adapted themselves to the job or situation, or may consider it not worth commenting on certain aspects, you should combine or follow your consultation with some observation of the users in action. Look for, and ask about, aspects that seem difficult, unusual or critical. Look also for informal modifications to the job, work space or equipment that the user may have made for themselves – for example a hand-made sign or label on a machine, additional loose cushions on a seat, and so on. You should also record relevant circumstantial information such as the user's age, sex, experience, the time of day, weather, and so on.

Also, an amazing amount of information relevant to the redesign of a product or system often can be gained from observing inexperienced users' attempts to cope. Inexperienced users can reveal potentially important problems, difficulties, or ideas of which experienced users will be unaware.

Finding an inexperienced user is not always easy, but there may be ways of lowering a user's normal level of experience by introducing some novel feature. Acting as an inexperienced user, and perhaps being made to look naïve or foolish, can be embarrassing, too. You should reassure your volunteers – and maybe yourself – you are looking for shortcomings in the product design, not in the users, and they should blame the design of the product, not themselves, for any difficulties.

Once you have found volunteers, give them only the basic objective they have to achieve, without any detailed instructions. Such an objective might be, 'programme this VCR to record a programme on BBC 1 from 9 pm to 10 pm next Wednesday' (assuming they are not familiar with the machine). Another objective may be, 'listen to the voice-mail message that has been received on this telephone, and send a short text reply'.

You need to observe and record carefully what the inexperienced user does. Get your volunteers to talk about the task as they attempt it. You may find it takes what you would regard as an extraordinary amount of time for an inexperienced user successfully to operate something you are familiar with yourself, and your volunteer may actually be unable to achieve a seemingly simple objective. Don't offer advice if your volunteers get stuck – unless it looks as though they will cause damage or an injury, or until it would be more fruitful to move on to the next stage of a sequence of operations. Try not to laugh or get angry. Remember the advice about blaming the design, not the user.

SAQ 10

There are two different procedures for carrying out user tests as described here, depending on whether you are using experienced or inexperienced users. Summarise the steps in each approach.

Example | Intuitive use of digital cameras

Remember the discussion about displays and controls in the previous section. The study reported below aimed to investigate just how intuitive are the controls on typical digital cameras. The study showed that intuitive use is actually based on previous experience, whether with similar products or with products with similar features and functions. Therefore knowledge of how to use products is transferred by users from one product to another. However, such knowledge transfer is not always appropriate – for example, remember the differences between operating gas and electric controls. Following are extracts from the study, which was part of a larger research project.

Figure 39 Front and back views of the type of digital camera used in the study of intuitive use

The term *intuitive use* has been widely used with respect to various products and systems but has not yet been adequately defined. Through an extensive literature review, it was concluded that intuition is a type of cognitive processing that is often unconscious and uses stored experiential knowledge (knowledge gained through prior experience). Intuitive use of products involves using knowledge gained through other products or experiences.

The test camera (Figure 39) was chosen as it has a mix of features, some of which are unique to this model and others that should be familiar to some users as they have been employed in other cameras, other digital cameras, and other products. Levels of user expertise were classified as expert, intermediate, novice and naïve with digital cameras, and five people were chosen for each level of expertise. None of the participants had encountered the camera used in the tests before the experiment began.

The participants were asked to complete two operations, each of which consisted of a number of tasks, and that between them involved use of most of the functions and features of the camera.

> Operation 1. Use the camera to take a photograph in autofocus mode using the zoom function.

> Operation 2. Find the picture you took. Erase your picture. Search through the other images stored in the camera to find a specified image. Zoom in on the image so that the details become larger.

The participants were asked to try to work out the operations for themselves because using the manual would mask the use of their past experience. As well as video recording the participants' use of the camera, the experimenter asked participants to think aloud as they performed the tasks.

The time taken by each participant to complete all operations, and the component tasks, was recorded, as well as aspects such as correct, inappropriate and incorrect use of camera features, and the number of uses of each feature that were intuitive. In the analysis of the video data, intuitive use was regarded as immediate use of a feature without conscious reasoning, with minimal or no verbalisation.

Immediately after the completion of the operations, a technology familiarity questionnaire was completed by the participant and a structured interview conducted. The technology familiarity questionnaire and the interview were designed to establish whether or not relevant past experience is transferable between contexts. For example, the participants were asked about whether and how often they used common consumer electronic products, and how much of the functionality of those products they used.

The results showed that features that were more familiar were intuitively used more often. For example, the power button showed a high level of familiarity and a high percentage of intuitive uses. The navigate function of the menu also showed a high percentage of intuitive uses and a high level of familiarity. The DISP function, which controls the displays on the LCD screen, showed a very low level of familiarity and a correspondingly low percentage of intuitive uses. Only experts who had used similar digital cameras picked up this function easily.

It was found that prior knowledge of features or functions of the camera allowed participants to use those features intuitively, whereas unfamiliar features or functions had to be figured out, which was more time consuming and effortful. From the results, it can be suggested that prior exposure to products employing similar features helped participants to complete the operations more quickly and intuitively. The camera transfers features from other digital products, so even expert users of digital cameras who had limited experience with other digital products completed the tasks more slowly and effortfully than novices with digital cameras who did have experience with the features employed in the camera from using other products.

These findings suggest that relevant past experience is transferable between products, and probably also between contexts. The participants with relevant past experience with the different features show faster and more intuitive use of those features, so it should be possible to conclude that relevant past experience has contributed to that. Therefore, including familiar features and controls in a product, in a way that is easy to follow and is consistent with the user's expectations according to their past experience, should support intuitive use of the product.

(Source: Blackler et al, 2003)

As well as conducting special experiments with selected users of a product or machine, it can be informative to record what happens during normal use, by making observations of typical users at work. This is sometimes called an ethnographic approach, because it relies on observing and recording people's normal, everyday behaviour.

Example   Around the photocopier

Two people, A and B, are making two-sided copies from a bound document (a magazine). They have already completed the first task of making an unbound master copy.

Speech	Actions
B: Okay, and then it'll tell us, okay, and … It's got to come up with the little start thing soon. (pause) Okay, we've done all that. We've made our bound copies. (pause)	
A: It'll go on though, I think. Won't it?	
B: I think it's gonna continue on, after it realises that we've done all that. (8 second pause)	
A: Then again, maybe we need to change the task description.	
B: What do you think?	Selects CHANGE
A: No.	
B: Okay, 'Proceed'.	Selects PROCEED
A: Maybe I should just lift it up and put it …	
B: How do we skip this then?	
A: … down again. Maybe it'll think we're done.	
B: (laughs) Oh, Jean.	
A: There.	Opens BOUND DOCUMENT AID

Speech	Actions
Okay, we've done what we're supposed to do.	Closes BOUND DOCUMENT AID
Now let's put this down. Let's see if that makes a difference.	
(Looks back to display)	
(laughs)	
It did something.	
B: Good grief.	

(Source: Suchman, 1987)

The above example shows how everyday machines can be quite baffling. The challenge for designers is to learn from such studies of normal behaviour, and to make products and machines easier to use. This example also shows the benefit, for user research, of having two users operating a machine together, because they voice and discuss, in a natural way, what they are trying to do and the difficulties they encounter. A single user usually works in silence, but can be asked to think aloud as they work, although that is a less natural and more self-conscious way of working.

The results of studies such as these have meant that office photocopiers have become easier to use, and more sophisticated in communicating to their users through displays and controls. For instance, our office photocopier now shows diagrams and text on a small display panel, explaining where problems have occurred, such as a paper jam, and illustrating step-by-step how to correct the problem.

Summarise key points of the section

Before reading my summary of the key points of this section, make your own summary in your Workfile.

Key points of Section 6

Methods of researching how people use products include personal user trips and immersion in product use, and observation of experienced and inexperienced users either in experimental or natural situations. These methods can provide useful information to guide product redesign and new product development.

Learning outcomes for Section 6 are 2.1, 2.2, 3.1 and 3.2.

This would be an appropriate point in your study of this block to refer to the video material on the course DVD relating to user research by the IDEO design team, and the people-centred research of Philips

7 Consumer choice

In Section 1 I said the individual consumer has little chance to influence the development of new products but the collective purchasing decisions of all of us individual consumers *are* influential on companies' product development plans, and ultimately on their commercial success. This section is about evaluating and choosing between different products, about making comparisons, and the influence of different personal values.

7.1 Product evaluation

Faced with so many new products continually becoming available, and continually being advertised, how can consumers choose between them? Perhaps some of the products you own you wish you had never bought because of the problems they gave you, or you wish that you had bought a different make or version of the product. Unfortunately, it is frequently only after personal experience of using a product for some time that you become aware of its shortcomings. Maybe when you were choosing it in the shop or showroom you had to make a choice based on little information and little or no opportunity to try it out before purchase.

This problem led to the rise of consumer tests of classes of products, exemplified in the UK by the Consumers' Association, with its *Which?* magazine test reports. These provide guidance for consumers by making comparative tests of similar products and recommending the product that offers the best value for money. As you probably realise, identifying value for money is not always easy. A straightforward comparison of identical products at different prices would be easy enough, but competing products are never identical in all respects.

What the *Which?* tests attempt to do is to provide as much objective information as possible about the measurable performance features of the product range, and then add assessments of less-measurable features in as rational a way as possible. A typical *Which?* report therefore lists firstly objective measures such as weight and dimensions, then the presence or absence of specific features, and then assessments of factors such as reliability or convenience. More subjective factors may also be included, such as the ride, handling or comfort of a motor car.

If you were trying to compare the reliability of a range of motor cars, what criteria would you cover and how would you assess individual cars on the criteria?

This is one of the tests the Consumers' Association carries out regularly. It identifies four main reliability criteria: (a) the number of days during any year the car is off the road for servicing or repairs; (b) the frequencies of breakdowns; (c) faults; and (d) mechanical problems. The association surveys a large number of its 1 000 000 members, asking them to provide this information for their own cars over the previous year. These data are then analysed and a three-point rating scale applied to each criterion: better than average, average, worse than average. The scores achieved in this way enable the Consumers' Association to list a large number of cars in reliability-rated groups.

Exercise 6   Evaluation factors

Suppose that you intend to make an evaluation of portable television sets, as an aid to choosing one to buy. What factors would you consider including in the evaluation?

Discussion

My own attempt at this began with a random list of factors. I jotted these down as soon as I thought of them:

price

ease of carrying

weight

size

picture quality

sound quality

appearance

convenience of use

Some of these seem to be at different levels of importance, or else to be closely linked – for example, the TV set's weight contributes strongly to its ease of carrying, and sound and picture quality could be considered together as performance. This recognition of different levels of criteria is quite normal, and can in fact be used to help expand the list. For example, thinking about convenience and performance led me to think of other aspects, or sub-criteria, of those criteria. My expanded list then became:

price

performance
    picture quality
    sound quality
    signal reception by inbuilt aerial

portability
    weight
    ease of carrying
    storage for mains lead

features
    text
    compatible with video games

convenience
    ease of use of controls (including remote)
    headphone socket

reliability

size
    screen size
    overall dimensions

appearance
    styling
    colours

safety

Although it is relatively easy to draw up such a list, it may not be easy to obtain measures or scores for all the factors. For instance, although price may be found quite easily for all the available TV sets on the market, reliability, or even weight, may be more difficult to find.

A criticism that might be made of this discussion of criteria for choosing TV sets is it concentrates on factors that seem relevant at the particular time that a decision is to be made, at the point of purchase. It ignores several potential criteria such as running costs, ease of maintenance and degradation of performance over time – criteria that may be unassessable at the point of purchase. A purchaser's assessment of a product will change over time, as he or she learns more about the product. I bought a kettle that looks good and seems to perform efficiently, but makes an annoyingly loud noise as the water begins to boil – I could not have known that at the point of purchase. The factors that influence a product assessment can be grouped into categories of pre-purchase, purchase, initial use and long-term use, as in Table 1 (Roy, 1990).

Table 1   Evaluating products over time: four groups of characteristics

Phase	Product design factors
before purchase	manufacturer's specification, advertised performance and appearance, test results, image of company's products, list price (brochure characteristics)
purchase	overall design and quality, materials, colours, finish, first impressions of performance, purchase price (showroom characteristics)
initial use	actual performance, ease of use, safety, etc. (performance characteristics)
long-term use	reliability, ease of maintenance, durability, running costs, etc. (value characteristics)

7.2   Making comparisons

Once a comprehensive set of relevant factors has been achieved, the next problem is making comparisons between different products. Some factors will be regarded as more important than others. For example, in comparing portable hairdryers for holiday use, the dryer's heat output may be less important than its overall size and weight, while the reverse may be the case for choosing a professional, salon-based hairdryer. For one person, the running costs of a car may be more important than reliability; for another person, fuel consumption may be less important than comfort.

People value (weight) product factors differently because they have different goals or objectives they are trying to achieve in choosing between products, and different requirements in using a product. Different people may therefore suggest completely different sets of criteria for evaluating the same product-type. In making an evaluation, therefore, it is first necessary to identify the particular set of factors that is regarded as relevant by the decision-maker.

Organisations such as the Consumers' Association carry out their evaluations of a wide range of products, and offer advice and recommendations relevant to most consumers. But users with special needs often need specialised evaluation reports. The example below contains extracts from a report prepared by the organisation called Ricability (which stands for research and information for consumers with disabilities).

Example	Choosing a vacuum cleaner that's easy to use

Weight

What to look for

If you have limited strength, the weight of the cleaner will be important, whichever type you decide on. Check to see the carrying handles are comfortable to grip and that you can carry the machine with two hands if necessary.

An automatic cord rewind is helpful: you pull out the length of cord you need and press a button that retracts it back into the cleaner. Manually stored cords can be unwound easily if the cleaner has a quick release hook, but still has to be wound up by hand.

Upright cleaners have a small hose attached to the back of the machine that you fix attachments to. With cylinder cleaners you use the hose for all types of cleaning so you don't have to take it on and off.

Whether lengths of tube push together or extend telescopically, they should require little force. Cleaning tools should fit on the end of the tubing easily – and should be easily removed and replaced in the cleaner storage area.

What we found

The weights mentioned in the machine assessments are of the cleaners with their attachments. We found those that were around 5 kg were also noticeably less bulky to carry. Of those tested, the Dyson cylinders were bulkier than the rest, although their carrying handles were longer, giving you space for two hands. On the upright cleaners, carrying handles were generally halfway up the back and were often covered by wound up electric cord.

The more force you use to push together the tubes and tools, the more strength you will need to pull them apart. With most of the cylinders, you simply pushed the hose in, but with some, detaching it involved squeezing both sides of the hose end. None of the tubes on the cleaners needed you to use great force to push them together. Telescopic tubing takes away the need to put lengths together, but it still required some strength to extend and collapse.

Storage space for small cleaning tools, such as an upholstery brush and crevice tool, was provided on the cleaners. Each one fitted into its own space, so they all required some precision to replace. We looked at the colour contrast of the tools and their storage area as good contrast makes it easier for you to replace the tools if you have poor sight.

Cleaning

What to look for

The shape and width of the cleaner's main handle, or the part of a cylinder's hose that is meant to be held, will affect how comfortable it is to use. Moulded gripping indentations should prevent your hands from slipping, but should not be so deep they require a specific handhold. If the handle is closed, there should still be enough space for a swollen or painful hand.

With an upright cleaner, you should be able to easily release the cleaning head from the upright section – part way down for general use and fully for cleaning under low furniture. Cleaners that are light to push are less tiring and if you have painful grip they are more comfortable than appliances that need pressure.

The tubing and tools should not feel too heavy if you are using them above ground level – for example, when cleaning upholstery or curtains.

What we found

On the cleaners we assessed we found that the controls were generally easy to find by colour or by touch. The on/off control on most of the cylinder cleaners was a large section of the top edge of the cleaner body. This was meant to be pushed by foot but you could also use your hands. Most of these controls were quite slippery, but their size and the fact they required only light pressure made them easy to use.

On/off controls on the upright cleaners were located on the main handles. These were either push buttons or switches. Those that protruded from the handle surface were easiest to locate and use. They varied in the strength needed to operate them.

To adjust the cleaning heads for carpet or hard floor use, or for different lengths of carpet pile, most of the cleaners had a control on the cleaning head. This was a protruding foot switch on the cylinder cleaners and a variety of types on the uprights. Some models had automatic height adjustments. Variable suction power is a useful extra if you need to clean curtains and rugs.

Dealing with the dust container/changing the filters

What to look for

Changing the dust container usually involves opening the cleaner, removing a dust bag from a holder, maybe emptying the bag and replacing it, or fitting a new one and putting everything back together again. From time to time the filters in the cleaner will also have to be changed. Ideally there should be space to allow you easy access to the bags and filters, no fiddly movements and no action requiring much strength.

What we found

No vacuum cleaner we tested had ideal dust and filter arrangements. One or other of the actions required was cramped or awkward on all the cleaners.

Most cleaners had throwaway dust bags that are easier and less messy to deal with than reusable bags. *Which?* reports that reusing bags reduces cleaning power. Gaining access to the bag and often the filters involved lifting a lid or lifting off a section of the cleaner body. On some of the cleaners this required some strength. Removing or replacing the dust bag was fiddly on many models. Since our initial report many more machines have switched to bagless systems and even filterless systems; we will look at these in more detail in our upcoming report.

If you have poor or painful grip

If you have poor or painful grip there are features on each machine that you will need to look at more carefully. The weight of the machine may be important to you, especially if you have lots of stairs in your house.

You will also need to look at the handles of the machines. Comfort is important so make sure you have enough space for your hands and see if you can hold the machine with two hands. With cylinder machines look at the grip on the tubing, it should have some moulding but not so much that you need to have a specific handhold.

Also look at the controls on the machine. If they are hand rather than foot operated, make sure they protrude well from the body of the machine and are not too stiff. Make sure the machine you buy does not have a bag or filter that is awkward to replace. If the vacuum cleaner does not have a bag, check what you need to do to empty the container and change the filter. The process of changing the bag or filter should not be too tricky or involve difficult hand movements.

If you have poor sight

If you have poor sight, there are some features of the machine you should look at in more detail. The tubing on the machines should fit together easily and not be complicated. Look at the cord, do you have to rewind it by hand or is it automatic? If you have to do it by hand, is this tricky? The controls should be easily visible, having good colour contrast with the body of the machine and project well from the surrounding area. The colour contrast of the tools is also important. Check to see how easy it is to change the bag and the filter, and how easy they are to get to.

(Source: **www.ricability.org.uk**)

7.3 Cost, price, value and values

Evaluation, as the word itself suggests, is essentially concerned with value. I have mentioned value for money, but I have steered clear of other types of value. The different weighting of evaluation factors by different people unavoidably involves personal preferences, background and experiences. Personal values are notoriously variable and difficult to establish. Although the price of a product may be easy to establish, its value may be more contentious. As Oscar Wilde commented, some people 'know the price of everything and the value of nothing'.

In terms of the examples referred to earlier, value might be perceived in the improved usability and appearance of the Frister and Rossman sewing machine, or the imagery and performance of the Mazda MX5 sports car.

It can be difficult to put a price on something that is valued highly; some things really are priceless. But in market economies, everything is assumed to have a price and its value is always assumed to be higher than its price. That is, a purchaser will not pay a higher price for a product than its value to the purchaser.

Where a product is in high demand, or is scarce, its price can rise close to its value. In other circumstances, such as falling raw materials prices or manufacturing costs, its value may remain high but its price may fall considerably. Normally, a seller has to keep the price greater than the product's cost to him or her, in order to make a profit. So, in most circumstances, a product's price is located somewhere between cost to the seller and value to the buyer. Buying something at cost price implies the seller has made no profit on the transaction. Hence, value, price and cost are related as in Figure 40.

In Figure 40 the lower, shaded portion of the bar represents all the costs to a producer (the seller). Figure 41 shows this cost is made up of base cost, plus the manufacturing cost that includes all the research, development and design work.

Given that a producer wants to maximise profit it has two options: lower the costs, or increase the value of the product so consumers might pay more for it. Both of these actions will increase the size of the top, unshaded portion of the bar and offer opportunities for greater profitability. This is where design activity is so valuable.

Design can contribute to a lowering of costs by creatively looking for opportunities to reduce or substitute materials, to reduce energy use, to combine components or achieve outcomes in different ways (Figure 42).

Design can also contribute to raising the value of products by making them work better, last longer, or in other ways more successfully match consumers' wants and needs. Hence, the skills of design can provide added value in products (indicated in Figure 43).

All successful product design companies use design, alongside research and development, in attempts to both lower costs and increase the value of their products.

In highly competitive world markets companies may use design activity as a normal part of maintaining their position in the marketplace rather than seeking to increase sales or profitability.

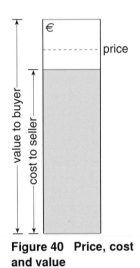

Figure 40   Price, cost and value

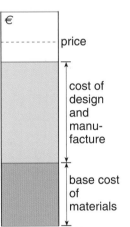
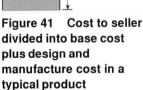

Figure 41   Cost to seller divided into base cost plus design and manufacture cost in a typical product

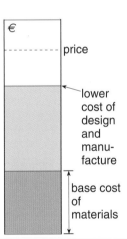

Figure 42   The ability for design to lower overall costs and thereby increase profit

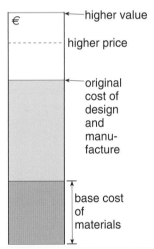

Figure 43   The ability for design to increase perceived value and thereby increase profit because the price can be higher

Where producer companies in a given market present consumers with products of similar technology with similar functions – for example digital cameras – then competition between companies tends to drive prices down, so the price line gets closer to the costs line. Some markets are particularly price-sensitive – purchasers choose between competing products according to price.

Some companies are happy to focus on offering a low-price product in order to maintain their market share. Other companies seek to offer high-value products as represented by performance, durability, reliability or appearance. For example, a manufacturer of portable power tools might decide to compete mainly either in the price-sensitive DIY market with keenly priced, basic specification and attractively styled tools; or in the less price-sensitive professional market with high performance tools. Their choice of market will have implications for the use of design in that company.

Purchasers are not always conscious of making choices and estimating values in quite the way that I have just described. However, in choosing one product rather than another at a similar price it is necessary to make a value judgement of the perceived benefits offered by the product. Such judgements are based on product *attributes* or characteristics – the factors used in evaluation, such as appearance, convenience or price. These characteristics arise from or are determined by the product's physical properties such as weight, size, shape, material, speed, power, surface finish, colour and range of functions. It is the embodiment of these *properties* in a particular product through its design that gives rise to its attributes, which in turn influence its perceived *benefits* or value. The relationships between properties, attributes and benefits are shown in Figure 44.

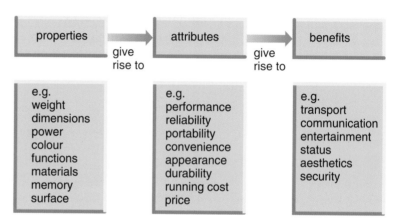

Figure 44   Relationships between properties, attributes and benefits of a product

I have tended to treat product evaluation as though it should be a fairly rational process. But as you and I know, our personal preferences and actual product purchase decisions are frequently far from rational. Certainly, I know that I have made impulse buys, or have discovered that product styling characteristics have carried more weight than I thought they would. Also, of course, there are the subtle pressures of advertising, peer-group pressures and the need to buy, use and display certain goods as a part of social interaction and communication.

Even the most rational of evaluation procedures cannot avoid questions of personal or social values, because the identification, selection and weighting of criteria are value-laden judgements. Not only will these judgements vary between different people, but also the same person's values will change over time. Sometimes, even quite radical shifts can occur in the values of large groups of people, as they become aware of environmental, technological, political or other issues that arise from product purchase decisions.

7.4 Designing for pleasure

In consumerist societies, buying, using and displaying products has come to represent a certain type of pleasure. This pleasure principle has to be acknowledged in new product development and design. The designer Kenneth Grange has said that a guiding design principle for him is that a product should be 'a pleasure to use'.

The pleasures of using a product are derived from the perceived benefits it offers to the user. Can we be more explicit in planning product benefits that are pleasurable? What is pleasure in this sense anyway? The following extract from Patrick Jordan's book *Designing Pleasurable Products* outlines four types of pleasure.

The four pleasures

A useful way of classifying different types of pleasure has been espoused by Canadian anthropologist Lionel Tiger. Tiger has made an extensive study of pleasure and has developed a framework for addressing pleasure issues, which he outlines in some depth in the book *The Pursuit of Pleasure*. The framework models four conceptually distinct types of pleasure – physical, social, psychological and ideological. Summaries of Tiger's descriptions of each are given below. Examples are added to demonstrate how each of these components might be relevant in the context of products.

Physio-pleasure

This is to do with the body and with pleasures derived from the sensory organs. They include pleasures connected with touch, taste and smell as well as feelings of sensual pleasure. In the context of products, physio-pleasure would cover, for example, tactile and olfactory properties. Tactile pleasures concern holding and touching a product during interaction. This might be relevant, for example, in the context of a telephone handset or a remote control. Olfactory pleasures concern the smell of the new product. For example, the smell inside a new car may be a factor that affects how pleasurable it is for the owner.

Socio-pleasure

This is the enjoyment derived from relationships with others. This might mean relationships with friends and loved ones, with colleagues or with like-minded people. However, it might also include a person's relationship with society as a whole – issues such as status and image may play a role here.

Products can facilitate social interaction in a number of ways. For example, a coffee-maker provides a service that can act as a focal point for a little social gathering – a coffee morning perhaps. Part of the pleasure of hosting a coffee morning may come from the efficient provision of well-made coffee to the guests.

Other products may facilitate social interaction by being talking points in themselves. For example, a special piece of jewellery may attract comment, as may an interesting household product, such as an unusually styled television set.

Association with other types of products may indicate belonging to a social group; the person's relationship with the product forms part of their social identity.

Psycho-pleasure

Psycho-pleasure pertains to people's cognitive and emotional reactions. In the case of products, this might include issues relating to the cognitive demands of using the product and the emotional reactions engendered through experiencing the product.

It might be expected that a word-processor that facilitated quick and easy accomplishment of, say, formatting tasks would provide a higher level of psycho-pleasure than one with which the user was likely to make many errors. The former word-processor should enable the user to complete the task more easily than he or she would with the latter. The outcome may also be more emotionally satisfying.

Ideo-pleasure

Ideo-pleasure pertains to people's values. Tiger refers to the pleasures derived from 'theoretical' entities such as books, music and art. In the context of products it would relate to, for example, the aesthetics of a product and the values that a product embodies.

A product made from biodegradable materials might be seen as embodying the value of environmental responsibility. This, then, would be a potential source of ideo-pleasure to those who are particularly concerned about environmental issues.

Ideo-pleasure would also include the idea of products as art forms. For example, the video cassette recorder that someone has in the home is not only a functional item, but something the owner and others will see every time they enter the room. The level of pleasure given by the video cassette recorder may, then, be highly dependent on how it affects its environment aesthetically.

(Jordan, 2000)

Summarise key points of the section

Before reading my summary of the key points of this section, make your own summary in your Workfile.

Key points of Section 7

Products can be evaluated in a variety of more or less objective ways, but a user's evaluation may change over time, from point of purchase to during long-term use.

People with different requirements and values will evaluate products differently.

People's requirements and values influence the benefits that they perceive to arise from a particular product. Those benefits are derived from the product's attributes, which are determined, through design, by the product's physical properties.

Perceived product benefits can be categorised under four types of pleasure: physio-, socio-, psycho- and ideo-pleasure.

Learning outcomes for Section 7 are 1.4 and 3.1

If you've not already done so, now would be a good time to return to the *Modelling Workbook* to complete Sections 4 and 5. The learning outcome for the *Modelling Workbook* is 4.1.

8

Design scenarios

So far we have looked at a variety of ways in which users' needs and preferences for new products can be identified and assessed. These needs and preferences have ranged from the physical to the psychological, from the practical to the conceited, from general needs to special needs. This section is concerned with how product planners and designers move from considering such information towards incorporating it into companies' product planning and the development of new products.

8.1   User profiles and personas

How can we draw together the varied needs and preferences, wishes and requirements into a model of users of a new product, and thereby provide some guidelines for the product designer? How can we use rather vague but interrelated sets of user preferences to identify the potential for new products to meet unsatisfied, and even unrecognised, user requirements?

One way is to construct *scenarios* for how a product might be used by different users. That means constructing some storylines of the users' lifestyle and requirements that relate to opportunities for new product development.

Design scenario writing begins with identifying the potential *user profiles* and *personas*.

A user profile summarises the characteristics of the user population that must be designed for. A user persona is a hypothetical, but well-defined, particular user within that population.

The techniques introduced in the sections on 'Design for the market' and 'Design for the user' provide starting points for identifying profiles and personas. For instance, you can observe the range of different users of a particular product. Or if you know some people who are likely to be users of a certain product type, you can draw upon your personal knowledge of these people, or you can ask them to complete a questionnaire about their lifestyle, likes and dislikes. Different product types will have different user profiles. The following example develops profiles and personas for customers of automatic teller machines (ATMs) that dispense cash and give bank information, and is taken from an Open University course on user interface design (M873 *User Interface Design and Evaluation*, 2001).

A profile of user or customer characteristics for ATMs is presented in Table 2.

The table reflects a true user profile in that it describes the whole user population in terms of the attributes or characteristics relevant to the design of the user interface. However, as it stands, it gets us only part way of the way to describing our users. What we now need to do is to break up this one large bunch of users into smaller groups. We will have a greater chance of arriving at a successful design if we focus on who the users of the system are than if we try to accommodate a large band of users and their different patterns of

ATM use. You probably use an ATM in a different way to your parents, say, and they will use an ATM in a different way to children or teenagers. So, let's have another pass through and try to really identify the users in this situation.

Table 2

User characteristics	ATM customer characteristics
age	will range in age from about 12 to 80 and older
sex	both male and female
physical limitations	may be fully able-bodied or may have some physical limitations in relation to hearing, sight, mobility, use of hands, and wheelchair use; will be of varying heights
educational background	may have only minimal educational qualifications and possess limited literacy and numeracy skills
computer/IT use	may have little or no prior experience of computer or IT use
motivation	may be very motivated to use the ATM, particularly if they can do their banking quickly and avoid queuing in the bank
attitude	attitudes to use may vary, depending on the service the ATM offers, the reliability of the technology itself and the attitude of users towards computers

Exercise 7   ATM customer characteristics

Look at the user profile for ATM customers in Table 2. Based on people you know – family members, friends or work colleagues – split the collection of customers in Table 2 into two or more different groups.

Discussion

Based on my knowledge of how various members of my family use ATMs, I split the collection into three smaller groups and profiled each as shown in Table 3. This is not the only way in which you could split the initial grouping into smaller groups. Depending upon whom you modelled your groups, you may only have two groups or you may have four.

The teens in my family generally use their account only once a week – to deposit their pocket money or to make a withdrawal if they have saved enough for a particular purchase. There are also occasions, such as Christmas and birthdays, where extra money is deposited. For the teens, using a card machine is cool and grown up, and it means they won't have to wait in line on Saturday mornings when the banks and building societies are already busy. The young adults in my family use ATM facilities like a purse. They withdraw small amounts of money frequently – maybe even several times a day – as and when they need it, rather than withdrawing a wad of cash they may lose or spend recklessly.

The family members between the ages of 25 and 50 are generally busy, working people. Banking is a necessary part of life but the quicker it can be done, the better. Waiting in bank queues is something to be avoided, and they prefer to withdraw enough money from an ATM to last several days.

The older members of my family bank even less often. They tend to make a single weekly cash withdrawal to cover the week's expenses, although where possible they prefer to get their money from a person rather than a machine.

Table 3

User characteristic	ATM customer characteristics by group		
	Teens and young adults	**Young adults to middle age**	**Middle age to senior citizens**
age	12 to 25	25 to 50	50 to 80+
sex	both male and female	both male and female	both male and female
physical limitations	may be fully able-bodied or may have some physical limitations in relation to, e.g., hearing or sight; will be of varying heights	may be fully able-bodied or may have some physical limitations in relation to, e.g., hearing or sight; will be of varying heights	may be fully able-bodied or may have some physical limitations in relation to say, hearing, sight, mobility or use of hands; will be of varying heights
educational background	may have minimal or no educational qualifications	may have only minimal educational qualifications	may have only minimal educational qualifications
computer/IT use	likely to have some prior experience of computer or IT use	may have little or no prior experience of computer or IT use	may have little or no prior experience of computer or IT use
motivation	probably very motivated to use the ATM; range of services required may differ considerably.	could be very motivated to use the ATM, especially if they can do their banking quickly and avoid queuing in a bank	could be very motivated to use the ATM, but would probably prefer to stand in a queue in the bank
attitude	probably very positive attitude depending on the range and quality of services offered and the reliability of the technology itself	attitudes to use may vary depending on the range and quality of services offered and the reliability of the technology itself	attitudes to use may vary depending on the range and quality of services offered and the reliability of the technology itself

In his book *The Inmates are Running the Asylum*, subtitled *Why Hi-Tech Products Drive Us Crazy and How to Restore the Sanity*, interaction designer Alan Cooper proposes the use of personas as an effective way of designing for a broad population. Personas are not real people; rather, they are imaginary examples of real users they represent. Cooper's key recommendation is:

> Develop a precise description of your user and what s/he wishes to accomplish ... The actual method that works sounds trivial, but it is tremendously powerful and effective in every case. We make up pretend users and design for *them*.

(Cooper, 1999)

In defining personas, Cooper recommends that you be as specific as possible about the made-up details, and that you give the persona a name. He gives each persona an image, whether it is a stock photograph from a photo library or a sketched caricature. All these details serve to make that persona a concrete person in the designer's mind, and in the minds of the design team. During the design process, the persona is referred to by name, rather than as the user.

Cooper suggests that a unique set of personas be defined for each individual project, which he refers to as the project's 'cast of characters'. Within a cast, you may also find it useful to have some personas that have been defined only as people whom you are not designing for. Every cast, though, should have at least one primary persona who is the focus of your design.

Exercise 8   ATM user personas

Create a persona for each of the three groups profiled in Table 3. The discussion for the previous exercise may help you get started.

Discussion

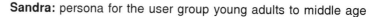

Here is my attempt.

Felix: persona for the user group teen/young adults

Felix is 13 years old. He gets pocket money every week, but spends it while out with his mates and there usually isn't anything left over to bank. He often gets money from his grandparents and uncles for his birthday and at Christmas, and this money is always deposited into his bank account. He saves this for more expensive or extravagant purchases; for example, he has a games console and likes to have the newest games. Plus he likes to be trendy, and have the newest jeans and trainers for knocking about in. Felix used to have an account with a savings passbook, but recently he has changed to an account that allows him to withdraw small amounts of money from ATMs.

Figure 45   Felix

Sandra: persona for the user group young adults to middle age

Sandra is 30 years old. She is married to Jason, and they have two children: Todd, aged 6, and Carly, aged 18 months. When Carly was born the family moved into one of the newly built housing estates in the town; local amenities such as shops, pubs, or a bank have yet to be built. This means that any shopping or banking must be done in the town centre, which is a six-mile round trip from the family home. Jason uses the car for work, and works long hours – he is often gone from 6 am to 8 pm. Sandra does not drive, and has to depend on public transport to get anywhere. She tries to do any errands, like shopping and banking, during Todd's school hours, as handling one child by public transport can be difficult especially with a pushchair, but it is far easier than trying to cope with two. More often than not she needs to make two trips to town on two separate days to get everything she needs. As there is an escalator in the bank, Sandra has to use the ATM for depositing and withdrawing money, and for checking the bank balance. This is in the front wall of the bank, and there is no canopy to protect customers from poor weather conditions.

Figure 46   Sandra

Maurice: persona for the user group middle age to senior citizen

Grandpa Maurice is 68 years old. He doesn't have a post office pension book; his pension is automatically credited to his bank account once a month. Every week he goes into the bank to withdraw enough cash for the week. While queuing is a bit difficult – he recently had a new hip – he does it because he prefers to get this money from a person. Also, he is not comfortable with technology; he does not have an ATM card. The amount he withdraws will include money to pay the milkman and the newsagent, and money to buy his pipe tobacco. This usually leaves him with a little cash in his pocket to last the week. All of his other bills, including the weekly shopping, are paid by cheque.

Figure 47   Maurice

8.1.1 Other stakeholders

We have discussed the profiling of primary users of a system, using either profiles or personas. While knowledge of the real direct end-users of a system is of the greatest importance, other people, distinct from the real users, may also have an interest or stake in the development of a product. In the information gathering process these various people are secondary users and are known as stakeholders. (Remember the discussion of 'Who are the users?' in Section 5.) Identifying stakeholders and gathering their requirements will often identify missed, conflicting, ambiguous, overlapping and unrealistic requirements.

SAQ 11

Can you think of any potential shortcomings in the use of personas in the process of new product design?

8.2 Product scenarios

User profiles and personas, and details of the stakeholders involved, can be used as the basis for stimulating ideas for new product development. The personas help provide a means for focusing on users and their requirements. Investigation and research techniques, such as user trips and user observation, can be combined with generating user profiles and personas in order to develop preliminary ideas for new product development.

For example, when the BBC wanted to explore the potential of digital audio broadcasting, it asked the design consultancy IDEO's London office to explore new digital radio product concepts. The team used scenario building to look at special purpose radios used by one person in different situations. One such scenario was developed around the user persona of Jean, whose work sometimes requires her to be on 24-hour call (Figure 48, overleaf). The designers then used this and other scenarios as a basis for developing new designs for digital radios, such as the one in Figure 49.

Figure 49   Concept design for a digital radio with features derived from Jean's scenario

scenario **1 Jean's emergency**   2.00 am

scenario
description   Jean is woken by a telephone call, it's an
emergency. She gets out of bed and
starts to get ready.
Jean switches on her personal digital radio in the
bathroom to help her wake up. It automatically
tunes into her usual channel for this time of the day.

key ideas   • specific stations for specific time – 'MYradio'

• agent driven learning system – watch me

scenario **2 In the car**   2.20 am

scenario
description   She gets into her car and docks her personal
digital radio to recharge the batteries.
The radio communicates her car-specific
listening preferences, via infra-red (IR) link,
to the in-car radio, so when she wants to listen
to music the car radio suggests her favourite station.
Her programme is interrupted by some travel news
but luckily it will not affect her journey.

key ideas   • car docking – powers battery

• infra-red link – personal radio can communicate
preferences to other radios

• environment specific information – in the car she
gets travel news

scenario **3 Back at home**   5–6.00 am

scenario
description   Jean arrives back home. As she moves from room
to room her digital radio automatically links to the
speakers in each room. She is listening to BBC
Radio Music Plus as usual for this time in the
morning.
Knowing she wants some music to go
jogging to later, Jean records some music from
the Fitness Channel. She stores it on a memory
disc as she may want to use it again.
The programme has already started but she is
able to record it from the beginning.

key ideas   • speakers with infra-red connection – auto,
manual settings

• audio download to storage

• recording from the start of programme

scenario **4 In her lounge**   12.05 pm

scenario
description   After her run, Jean rests in the lounge and browses
the latest copy of Digital Radio Times. This
magazine is downloaded once a week and gives
Jean scheduling information as well as interesting
articles. She sets her digital radio to view through
her projector so she can see the text easily.
As she views the schedule information, different
programmes are subtly highlighted due to her
preference and previous listening habits. She
scans the information both visually and audibly.

key ideas   • visual manipulation of information to show preference

• audio visual magazine

• bulk download – probably at night

• projected displays

Figure 48   Digital radio use scenario developed for the persona of shift-worker Jean

Sometimes, product planners and designers develop personas
through the use of lifestyle collages, similar to the Japanese example
in Section 3. The collage illustrated in Figure 50(a), was developed as
part of the planning for a new shaver. The central persona is fleshed
out graphically with pictures of people, products and lifestyle
situations that influence that persona's relationship with the potential

new product. Later, in advertising the shaver, similar collages were used as in Figure 50(b) to associate the product with a sense of a typical user's lifestyle.

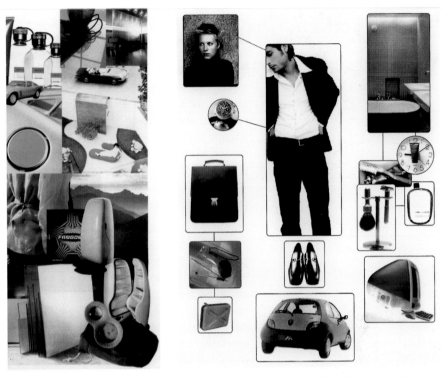

(a) Lifestyle collage developed during a concept design study

(b) Advertisement for the developed product in a similar style

Figure 50　Design and marketing of a shaver

In the example below, observation of elderly people using the equipment in their kitchens led to the development of a persona named Mary, and an identification of a particular problem that she, and millions like her, has in using her oven. The example develops a scenario for a new product, or product opportunity (potential product).

Example　Cooking aid

Phase 1

Persona

Mary is 70 years old and lives alone. She loves to bake and often entertains her family for holidays. She has developed arthritis and is no longer comfortable reaching into the oven to lift things out. Losing the ability to bake things has been depressing for her to contemplate. Mary is hesitant to have her family over and no longer feels confident entertaining in her home.

Product opportunity

Saying that you are going to improve the way elderly people use an oven is a general statement that leaves too much variation. Saying that you are going to design a tool that electromechanically lifts food out of an oven is too specific. A balanced statement would be more like this: the product opportunity is to improve the way elderly women lift things out of the oven.

Components of the scenario

The product is for older women who have lost the strength and flexibility to lift. They become the core market. A review of the literature should focus on this group. The expert advisers for this programme are healthcare workers who work with the elderly and doctors that work with seniors and are experts in rheumatology. It is also important to know about ovens, specifically the type of ovens that older women might own. It also requires looking at (designing for disability) guidelines. Other stakeholders are people who install ovens and sell appliances, organisations that promote products for seniors, and doctors and healthcare workers that might prescribe this for patients. The primary customer base is the women themselves; it is important to find women that fit in this category. Some may have already developed naïve but novel ways of addressing the opportunity. Although applicable to men as well, the majority of the elderly population is female. Any particular issues for women may make the product better meet the majority needs, wants, and desires of this population.

Through the combination of the statement and scenario, the team now has the directions of where to look for gaining a better understanding of how a product may improve this situation. However, there is no clear sense of what the product might look like, how it should be powered, and what material it would be made out of. The opportunity statement and the scenario will be revisited to make sure it is being adhered to and it serves as the core of the team's understanding of the programme. Both the opportunity statement and scenario continue to evolve after each phase.

Phase 2

The scenario established (above) would be developed further and the product opportunity statement would be clearer. The scenario would sound more like:

> Mary has arthritis in the lower spine and shoulders that limits her range of motion. She also has lost strength in her back and arm muscles. A device is needed that fits in the context of a standard oven that will compensate for her limited motion and reduced strength, and allow her to easily put in and remove a variety of pans and baking dishes in the oven. The device will have to lift items that range in weight from 1 – 15 pounds (0.5 – 7 kg).

The product opportunity statement may now sound like:

> The team will develop a product that will integrate with a standard oven and will be easy to install and clean. It must have a simple mechanism and must cost no more than $50 to buy and install. Any installation should be easy enough for a family member to do. While the primary market will be senior women with arthritis between the ages of 70 and 85, the primary purchasers may be family members.

At this point, the scenario and product opportunity statement are complemented by a series of models, diagrams, facts, and statements gleaned from research documents, which frame out the issues that will serve as the guidelines for assessing the concepts developed (later). For example, the size of standard ovens will be known and the team will know that a typical oven hasn't changed in size in close to 50 years.

(Source: Cagan and Vogel, 2002)

Summarise key points of the section

Before reading my summary of the key points of this section, make your own summary in your Workfile.

Key points of Section 8

Having defined and profiled a target user population, a range of personas can be developed as a way of focusing on the product's different likely users and their requirements. A persona is a hypothetical, but well-defined, example of a user.

How such personas would use a potential new product can be explored through scenarios. Such scenarios can help in generating ideas for new product development opportunities.

Learning outcomes for Section 8 are 1.3, 2.3 and 3.3.

This would be an appropriate point in your study of this block to refer to the material on the course DVD relating to developing personas.

9 The design brief

In most commercial practice, the formal starting point for the actual design of a new product is the design brief. Although it is an important step in the product planning and development process, it does not always get the attention it deserves. This section outlines the requirements and features of a good brief for a new product design, and some procedures to help in preparing such a design brief.

9.1 Writing a brief

A design brief is the instruction to the designer from the client to take on a project, and some background information on the decision to initiate the project. However, in many examples of product design this instruction is brief in another sense – it contains little information.

In some cases there may be good reasons for the brevity of the design brief. Many so-called new products are in fact just modifications of existing designs, and the brief may be just an instruction to replace a component such as a motor with a different version, or to redesign the product's outer casing. Also, in some cases, a company's management structure may be such that just a few people, such as the marketing and/or technical director, may be involved in the design brief decision-making – which may be just a verbal discussion.

However, research (Walsh et al, 1999) has shown that the more commercially successful companies tend to pay more attention to drafting a formal design brief, and developing this into a clear and careful product design specification, than do the less successful companies.

The design brief, then, is an important step in the clarification of just what a new product is expected to be and to do. It is not, of course, a statement of the design *solution* – which is what the designer will eventually generate – but a statement of the design *problem* or *opportunity*. Some of the relevant aspects of a design brief were included in the product-opportunity statements for an oven lifting aid, in the previous section.

A typical example of a design brief might be something like the following, from a domestic furniture manufacturer.

Example **Domestic computer trolley**

The continued growth of home computing and home working suggests there is an expanding market for an item of furniture: a domestic computer work trolley. Such a trolley would be capable of accommodating, in appropriate positions, the computer unit itself; a monitor; keyboard; printer; other peripherals, such as a scanner; a separate disk drive; storage boxes for disks; and a telephone modem. Potential users are both adults and children from age 12. Selling price must be not more than £100 and probably should be in the range of £80–90. The product should be available in retail outlets in nine months' time. Problems of form and aesthetics are seen to arise from:

(a) the conflict between high-tech computer aesthetics and normal domestic furniture aesthetics;

(b) the premium on space that normally exists in likely places of use such as children's bedrooms and adults' studies.

Notice this brief does tend to suggest a particular type of solution, a trolley, to what might in fact have been treated as a more open-ended design problem, such as furniture for home computers. However, the client company has apparently done some preliminary market research, and has identified a likely selling price range, the user population and the range of equipment to be accommodated. It has also identified problems of form and aesthetics. It is also clear that a lot more work still needs to be done to specify more precisely the weight, volume and dimensions of typical equipment items, anthropometrics of users and the ergonomics of computer use, and potential materials and manufacturing methods for the trolley.

The design brief is therefore an intermediate stage between the fundamental or underlying product idea and a full specification of the requirements the product is expected to satisfy. Crucially, the brief sets the design *goal*, outlines the *context* in which the new product must operate, identifies the major *constraints* within which the design goal must be achieved, and suggests some *criteria* by which a good design proposal might be recognised. The difference between constraints and criteria is that constraints set specific, usually quantitative, targets or limits for the product designer, while criteria are more flexible and might be used for judging between different product design proposals, each of which meets the specific constraint targets. Constraints and criteria are sometimes expressed as demands and wishes in a design brief. Demands have to be satisfied in the final design, together with satisfying as many wishes as possible.

SAQ 12

Identify the goal, the context, the constraints, and the criteria in the design brief for the domestic computer trolley.

Exercise 9   Writing a design brief

Write a design brief for the oven lifting aid featured in Section 8. Write it in the style of the computer trolley brief, above, ensuring it identifies the design goal, its context, the major constraints, and relevant criteria.

Discussion

Here is my attempt.

Many elderly people experience difficulty with lifting things into and out of their ovens. This spoils their enjoyment of an everyday task, cooking, and restricts their independence in being able to perform such a task. The difficulties can be due to a variety of physical factors such as arthritis and rheumatism in hands, arms and back, muscular weakness, and limitations in movements such as bending and reaching. The product required is therefore to be an oven use aid especially for older women (between 70–85 years), to assist lifting things such as baking trays or casserole dishes into and out of standard, conventional ovens. The weight of items that have to be lifted and supported varies between 0.5–7 kg. Selling price should be not more than £35. Purchasers may well be younger family members, buying on behalf of their parents. Installation of the product should be possible with minimum do-it-yourself skills by family members. Use of the product should be simple and direct, easy and non-worrying for users. The product should be – and appear to be – robust and safe.

This brief might be summarised in terms of the design goal, context, constraints and criteria as follows.

Goal: an aid to assist lifting things into and out of domestic ovens

Context: elderly people, especially women, using their ovens for everyday cooking

Constraints: – usable by most women aged 70–85
  – selling price not more than £35
  – can lift and support a range of cooking pots, baking trays, etc. weighing between 0.5 kg and 7 kg
  – integrates with standard conventional ovens
  – safe
  – do-it-yourself installation

Criteria: – attractive to purchasers as well as users
  – simple to use
  – robust and conveys a safe appearance

9.2   The design before the design

Writing a design brief is a creative activity that is critical to the whole design process. Jens Bernsen, of the Danish Design Centre, has described the formulation of the brief as 'the design before the design'. By that he means:

> ... the decisive step in the development of a new product often occurs before the project begins ... Such design before the design does not appear spontaneously nor is its realisation separate from the whole process of creation. It is part of it.

(Bernsen, 1996)

The development and elaboration of the brief proceeds through the initial exploration of concepts and ideas by the design team, with clients, managers and designers working together. Bernsen's key points of a good design brief include the following.

Identify what the new product aspires to be

Ask what the product should be if it did not exist but had to be thought out from the beginning. This goal may be unobtainable. But even if it cannot be reached, it can provide valuable ideas for the brief on the new product.

Seek to identify The Big Idea of the new product in the design brief.

Describe the basic function of the product

More and more products contain a multiplicity of functions that are seldom or never used. At the same time, operating the product's basic functions may have become complicated or unclear.

Describe the typical and basic functions and make it a requirement that they should be completely or almost completely self-explanatory. It is necessary to decide what is essential and what is non-essential and to discard superfluous functions.

See the product the way the user sees it

If necessary, describe the use of the product via a series of scenarios for its application and for the situations it creates or is a part of. Try to identify the features of the product that are most important to the user.

Speak with some typical users of the product and with different types of users. Examine any complaints that may have been made by dissatisfied users or retailers. This can be a source of useful ideas for describing the way the user would like to experience the product.

Also remember in the brief that 'the user' of a new product usually is – and should be – many types of users, including children, the elderly or disabled users.

Describe the personalities of user and product

The typical user may be a member of a certain profession or belong to a certain group with respect to lifestyle or taste.

Form a picture of the typical user of the product. This implies the design brief may include references to a national, regional or international market and to certain user profiles within this market.

It is crucial that the product suit the environment in which it is to be used and that there be compatibility between the personalities of user and product.

It may be necessary to choose between satisfying a large number of users to a certain extent or fully satisfying a smaller number, ignoring the rest. The economically correct thing to do depends on the product and the market. But the choice should be a conscious one.

Describe the features that determine the experienced value

A product's design is often referred to as if it had to do only with its visual character. This is not the case. The user also experiences a product through its sound, weight, odour and, perhaps, taste, and he infers its invisible qualities via direct experience of those qualities that are immediately comprehensible.

The idea of a new product also depends upon how the user interacts with it. The use of any tool both requires and develops skills, and its interplay with the user or users can have a decisive impact on its experienced value.

Tell a good story: create a product idea that can be communicated

Build a good story into the product.

Many of the most successful products are the carriers of a Big Idea, something for which the product is remembered. Try to isolate such a principle in the product brief and make it into a central element in the communication that will subsequently accompany the product.

Concentrate the brief on the essential things

A good brief will concentrate on what is essential. It will also distinguish between primary and secondary wishes and demands.

Design is seldom a matter of satisfying every conceivable demand. Normally design is a matter of achieving a suitable balance between various wishes and demands and of doing the essential things properly. Non-essential and peripheral demands cause harm in a design brief because they take up space and deflect attention from what is really important.

Revise the brief from time to time

A good brief is a good starting point for developing a new product. This said, it is also necessary to realise that product design briefing is not an activity that is only relevant at the beginning of the project. Briefing is a dynamic process.

Many products are developed in stages where the big, important demands are fulfilled before the less important ones are approached. This means there may be a need for design briefs at several stages in the development process. In addition, the goals laid down by the brief at the beginning of the development project are not necessarily the final goals. They are, rather, the goals as they appeared before their significance to the finished product became clear.

Everybody who takes part in a development project learns something along the way about what the new product ought to be. Use this knowledge to revise the brief from time to time, as new goals are revealed. Not too often, but when necessary.

Keep in mind that a good brief describes a wish or a demand and never the solution itself.

(Bernsen, 1996)

Although presented from a different point of view, Bernsen's key points about establishing a brief overlap with many of the concepts and approaches presented earlier in this block.

Summarise key points of the section

Before reading my summary of the key points of this section, make your own summary in your Workfile.

Key points of Section 9

A design brief is a statement of the design problem or opportunity, not the design solution. The brief sets the design goal, context, constraints and criteria.

Preparing the design brief – the design before the design – is a creative activity and can result in an inspirational document for the design team.

Learning outcomes for Section 9 are 1.4, 2.3, 2.4, 3.3 and 3.4.

10 Product design specification

I suggested in Section 9 that the design brief is an intermediate stage between the basic product idea and a more complete specification of requirements. A *product design specification* is a further development of the brief into a comprehensive document that includes not only the outline of the design goal and the major constraints and criteria but also the more precise limits set for the complete range of performance requirements for the new product. This final section of the block is concerned with this step of developing from the design brief into the design specification.

A full product design specification will contain a lot of technical information and requirements, as well as many less-technical requirements, such as user population information and marketing factors. It is therefore quite common to distinguish between a *technical specification* and a *marketing specification* for a product design.

The marketing specification emphasises the requirements of:

- the user – with requirements such as function and performance;
- the purchaser – with requirements such as price, product life and maintenance;
- the producer company itself – with requirements such as design and production timescale, materials and manufacturing methods.

The technical specification translates these requirements into quantitative measures where possible and precise descriptions, and sets limits and standards.

Whereas the marketing specification deals with the desired *attributes* of a product, the technical specification deals more with the physical *properties* that will achieve these attributes. (Distinctions between attributes and properties were explained in Section 7.) Here, I shall concentrate more on marketing than on technical specifications.

10.1 Specifying benefits and requirements

An important step towards developing a design specification for a new product is to make an analysis of the *benefits* the identified users might expect to acquire from a new product.

The following specification of benefits for a camera was developed by Patrick Jordan in his book *Designing Pleasurable Products*, using his framework of the four pleasures introduced in Section 7. The required product benefits are derived from information or assumptions about the user characteristics of the target group for the camera.

Notice other important benefits are not being considered at this point. Some of those not being considered are technical benefits relating to the quality of the resulting photographs, or the range of distances or lighting situations for which the camera might be used.

Example	A still camera for women

Target group

Imagine the target user group for the camera is Western women aged between twenty-five and thirty-five of high socio-economic status. Given this is the target group, what are the implications in terms of product requirements? What follows is a four-pleasure analysis, suggesting some issues that may be of importance in this context and considering what the associated design requirements might be.

Physio-pleasure

A camera is a hand-held device. Clearly, then, the feeling of the camera in the hand may be a source of physio-pleasure to the user.

Product benefit: camera should feel good in the hand.

A camera is a product that people are likely to want to carry around with them. This is likely to hold for this target group as much as for any other.

Product benefit: camera should be easy to carry around.

When taking a photograph, the user will hold the camera to her face and look through the viewfinder. Here the camera may come into contact with parts of the face, in particular the side of the nose and the eyebrow. Again, the camera has come into contact with the body and should fit well against the face and be comfortable.

Product benefit: fits well and comfortably against the face.

Finally, for this example, the designers should be aware that many young women may have long fingernails. Clearly, they will not want these broken when using the camera.

Product benefit: camera should be operable with short and long fingernails without causing damage.

Socio-pleasure

A pocket camera is something that will often be used in a social context. The user may want to take photos of her friends and loved ones. She is also likely want to take photos in public places, where other people will see her using the camera.

A major social issue here is the impression of the user the camera gives to others. Our target users are of a high socio-economic status. Perhaps they wish this to be reflected in the design of the camera. If they have paid a lot of money for the camera, then the camera's design should reflect this. In this way the camera can act as a badge saying, 'I'm a successful person'.

Product benefit: camera should confer the impression of high socio-economic status on the user.

As a target group that may be particularly image-conscious, it may also be that this group is concerned not only with socio-economic status, but also with cultural status. In other words, the design should give the impression the user has not only affluence, but also a measure of good taste.

Product benefit: camera should confer the impression of high cultural status on the user.

The social context in which the camera is used may also have implications for the benefits the camera should provide the user with. Presumably, these users will be mainly taking pictures of people they know, or places they are visiting, rather than of professional models. Models may be prepared to spend a considerable amount of time getting a pose just right and waiting while the photographer makes adjustments to the camera settings in order to get the shot just right. The chances are, however, that our users' friends and families will not be prepared to wait while she goes through such a rigmarole. This indicates that the camera's design should support her in taking pictures quickly.

Product benefit: camera should enable the user to take photos quickly.

Another socio-issue connected with camera use is the potential noise disturbance to others that taking a photograph may create. People may want to take photos in places such as churches, concert halls or theatres where disturbance would not be appreciated. Indeed, it may be a cause of embarrassment to the user and of annoyance to others. This may just as likely be an issue for this target group as for any other.

Product benefit: camera should be operable without disturbing others or embarrassing user.

Psycho-pleasure

An issue to consider here is the pleasure associated with taking the photos and the enjoyment of the outcome. Much of this may be associated with traditional usability issues, such as effectiveness and efficiency of performance. In this case, effectiveness may be associated with the quality of the photos, while efficiency may be about how easy it is to take the photos.

Again, it is important to consider the quality of photographs these people will be after. As they are not professional photographers, they will probably be after good quality snaps rather than professional-quality photographs. While a professional photographer may be prepared to spend hours getting a shot just right, these users will probably not be prepared to spend a long time over a shot, no matter how good the outcome. The emphasis, then, should be on getting the shot right with minimal effort. This reinforces the point that arose under socio-pleasure, about the camera's design supporting quick operation.

Product benefit: camera should enable the user to take photos quickly.

Our users are young, dynamic, successful women. They probably don't have the time or inclination to sit down and spend a lot of time acquainting themselves with the camera before using it. Compared with many of the electronic and information technology products that people now use in their daily lives, a camera seems an inherently simple product. It seems unlikely – particularly for this user group – that people would be willing to tolerate a camera they cannot pick up and use at the first attempt.

Product benefit: camera should be easy to use at the first attempt.

Ideo-pleasure

Choosing to use or buy a particular product over another may often represent an ideo-decision – a decision that reflects the tastes, values and aspirations of the purchaser. Here, those involved in the product creation process should be aware of the potential ideo-perspectives of the successful young women at whom the camera is targeted.

First, it seems sensible the product should provide aesthetic pleasure to those for whom it is designed – those involved in the design process should, then, give some consideration to the issue of the sorts of aesthetics this target group might like.

Product benefit: camera should give aesthetic pleasure.

Another issue affected by life today might be the extent to which the user would wish the product to be a reflection of her femininity. Twenty or thirty years ago overtly feminine designs may have been seen as patronising. These attitudes are reflected, for example, in the feminist literature of the 1970s, much of which viewed popular culture – including design – as a framework within which women were controlled and patronised by men ... As women increasingly win equality and make socio-economic progress, many may also feel it less contentious to express their femininity through the products they own and use. Indeed, the percentage of women working in design is ever increasing. These factors have led to a climate where 'feminine' design may be seen as positive and expressive, rather than patronising. Such attitudes are reflected in post-modern feminism, which tends to support the cultural representation of gender differences to a far greater extent than did the 1970s feminist movement ...

Product benefit: camera should reflect the users' femininity.

Aside from personal ideologies, such as self-perceptions and aesthetic preferences, people's pleasure with products may be affected by their social, political and religious ideologies. An issue that seems likely to concern a young, well-educated group such as this is the environment.

Product benefit: camera should be environmentally 'safe'.

So, by considering the characteristics of the target group holistically, it has been possible to make some assumptions about the sorts of benefits they may wish to gain from the product under consideration. In summary, the product specification derived from this example is listed below.

Product benefits specification for a photo-camera design for European women of a high socio-economic status aged between twenty-five and thirty-five years.

- Camera should feel good in the hand.
- Camera should be easy to carry around.
- Camera fits well and comfortably against the face.
- Camera should be operable without causing damage to the users' fingernails.
- Camera should confer the impression of high socio-economic status on the user.
- Camera should confer the impression of high cultural status on the user.
- Camera should enable the user to take photos quickly.
- Camera should be operable without disturbing others or embarrassing user.
- Camera should be easy to use at the first attempt.
- Camera should give aesthetic pleasure.
- Camera should reflect the users' femininity.
- Camera should be environmentally 'safe'.

In total, then, this product benefits specification contains twelve potential benefits against which the quality of proposed design solutions can be judged. Notice that in the list, no indication has been given of the pleasure category with which each of the benefits is associated. This is not important now. The four-pleasure framework was used as a means of structuring thought in order to arrive at the product benefits. However, once the specification has been decided, the framework has served its purpose. From now on the issue is about how to provide these benefits through the design of the product.

(Source: Jordan, 2000)

SAQ 13

For a user group of teenagers, suggest at least one desired product benefit in each of the four pleasures (as above) for the domestic computer trolley for which a brief was suggested in Section 9.

Most of the benefit statements in the example above offer little more than vague suggestions of what the assumed product user would like to experience in using the product. A further step towards a full product design specification would be to refer to more specific product *requirements* the user is looking for.

The example below shows how to develop users' statements about the benefits they want into more precise statements of requirements for the product design specification. The product to be designed was an electric screwdriver. The team conducted interviews with prospective users of such a screwdriver, and then carefully converted the 'customer statements' about needs and wishes into 'interpreted needs' that are more specific statements about the required aspects to be designed into the new product.

Example	Electric screwdriver

The customer data template below is filled in with sample customer statements and interpreted needs or product requirements from these statements. Some of the interpreted needs have been omitted here, as part of a following exercise that asks you to make your own attempts at converting customer statements into interpreted needs. First, read the template entries to see how the design team interpreted customer statements into needs statements. The customer statements are typically statements about what the customer wants, or uses the tool for. The interpreted needs are statements of what the tool should be able to do, hence product requirements.

Notes

This template represents a partial list from a single interview. A typical interview session may elicit more than 50 customer statements and interpreted needs. SD is an abbreviation for *screwdriver*.

Customer: Bill Esposito

Interviewer(s): Jonathan and Lisa

Address: 100 Memorial Drive

Date: 19 December

Currently uses: Craftsman Model A3

Type of user: Building maintenance

Question/Prompt	Customer statement	Interpreted need
Typical uses	I need to drive screws fast, faster than by hand.	The SD drives screws faster than by hand.
	I sometimes do duct work; use sheet metal screws	[See exercise below]
	Do a lot of electrical: switch covers, outlets, fans, kitchen appliances.	The SD can be used for screws on electrical devices.
Likes – current tool	I like the pistol grip; it feels the best.	[See exercise below]
	I like the magnetised tip.	The SD tip retains the screw before it is driven
Dislikes – current tool	I don't like it when the tip slips off the screw.	The SD tip remains aligned with the screw head without slipping.
	I would like to be able to lock it so I can use it with a dead battery.	The user can apply torque manually to the SD to drive a screw.
	Can't drive screws into hard wood.	[See exercise below]
	Sometimes I strip tough screws.	The SD does not strip screw heads.
Suggested improvements	An attachment to allow me to reach down skinny holes.	The SD can access screws at the end of deep, narrow holes.
	A point so I can scrape paint off screws.	The SD allows the user to work with screws that have been painted over.
	Would be nice if it could punch a pilot hole.	[See exercise below]

(Source: Ulrich and Eppinger, 1995)

Exercise 10   Interpreting needs

One interpreted need has been omitted in each of the four categories of 'Question/Prompt' in the data template above. Make your own suggestion for each of the missing interpreted needs, using the blank cells in the template below. The interpreted-need statements are requirements of the product. A new design for the product could be evaluated against such requirements to see if they are satisfied or not.

Customer statement	Interpreted need
I sometimes do duct work; use sheet metal screws.	
I like the pistol grip; it feels the best.	
Can't drive screws into hard wood.	
Would be nice if it could punch a pilot hole.	

Make your own entries above, before reading the entries that were made in the original study, below.

Customer statement	Interpreted need
I sometimes do duct work; use sheet metal screws.	The SD drives sheet metal screws into metal duct work.
I like the pistol grip; it feels the best.	The SD is comfortable to grip.
Can't drive screws into hard wood.	The SD can drive screws into hard wood.
Would be nice if it could punch a pilot hole.	The SD can be used to create a pilot hole.

10.2 Specifying attributes and properties

It is the final, detailed design proposal for a product that ultimately specifies the product. The detailed design drawings and notes specify the actual dimensions, shapes, materials, colours and features, as they will be embodied in the product. The prior statements of a product design specification offer goals and guidelines to the designer, but the designer has to imagine and decide how to achieve the goals. As I explained in Section 7, the designer fixes the product properties, in order to achieve the attributes and benefits desired by the user.

In setting requirements for a new design, writing a product design specification therefore involves judgement on setting appropriate limits to the designer's freedom. What is most important is it specifies attributes and properties in terms of the required product performance, but without specifying a particular solution. In other words, it specifies what the product must do, but not what it must be; it specifies *ends*, but not *means*.

An example of inappropriate design specification might be to say that a work-surface should be made of marble. It may well be that marble is an appropriate material, but there may also be many others such as metals, plastics or ceramics. The requirements for the surface may be that it should have a smooth texture, be resistant to knocks and light blows, and easy to clean; these could be satisfied by several different materials. However, there may also be other properties and attributes to marble as a material that are important, such as colours and perceived status.

Specifying the required product performance needs careful thought, research and perhaps testing. It is not adequate simply to guess at the required performance, nor just to take it from an existing product. Inevitably there will be both quantitative and qualitative requirements, but wherever possible the specification should be expressed in quantified terms. For example, rather than leaving a vague requirement statement such as 'lightweight', a maximum acceptable weight should be specified. Also, wherever possible and appropriate, a specification should set a range of limits within which acceptable performance lies. So a specification should not state height 425 mm, if a range between 400 mm and 450 mm is acceptable.

A reliable and comprehensive performance specification therefore takes some effort to compile and requires careful research into a wide range of requirements from users and other stakeholders such as purchasers, retailers, distributors and manufacturers. The example below shows how to develop a performance specification for a required product benefit such as, 'it should be portable'.

Example	Portable fax machine

Communication devices of various kinds have proliferated, especially with the growing use of radio and satellite communications links, data transfer by telephone, Internet communications, and so on. Many communications devices first appeared as large, office-based, immobile machines, and then gradually became smaller, lighter, and portable. Telephones and computers are classic examples; so too is the fax machine. Some people now need to have not only one at the office and one at home, but also one that can be used at other locations and therefore travels with them. This example is based on the design of such a portable fax machine.

There are many specialised aspects that would have to be researched and specified, such as the industry communication standards, or scanning and printing devices to be incorporated. We shall concentrate here primarily on the key attribute of 'portable'. What exactly does this mean? We need to know what features of portability might be important to potential purchasers and users of the fax machine.

We therefore interview a range of fax machine users, and potential new users of a portable facility, about their needs. Typical users for a portable fax machine are business representatives, engineers or others who have to travel in their work and communicate with their head office or other locations by means of documents such as drawings or order forms. From this it emerges that there are two distinct aspects to portability. The first is, quite simply, that the machine can be carried and used comfortably and easily. The second aspect is that the purpose of a portable machine is it can be used in a wide variety of different locations – perhaps clients' offices, construction sites and suppliers' factories. The portability attribute is therefore strongly related to usability of the machine in such environments.

Further research with users is necessary to develop performance specifications for both of these aspects of portability. For example, to specify the carryable performance features, it is not adequate simply to suggest a carrying handle. Nor is it adequate just to weigh a rival product and specify that as a maximum weight. We need to know the range of users for the fax machine and the typical distances or lengths of time it might be carried. Experiments with a few representative, least-strong users and maximum expected carrying times could then establish an appropriate weight limit.

We also need to investigate further the variety of locations in which it is desired to use the fax machine. One aspect of the typical use of such a machine is it is not always possible to use it on a desk or other stable surface. Sometimes, as with portable computers, use includes on someone's lap on a train or in an airport lounge. Therefore the machine must be small but stable. Does some potential use include during meetings or conferences, for example by journalists faxing press releases? In that case its operation should be silent or very quiet. Does it include out-of-doors use? In that case there might be weatherproofing requirements, or the user might be wearing gloves, with implications for the design of buttons, controls, paper feed mechanisms, and so on.

Obviously, in many locations there is no available power source, and so a portable fax machine must have its own batteries. But it may be that salespeople and others often use the fax machine in their car, and therefore the car's battery could be used through the cigarette-lighter socket. Another aspect of performance that emerges is that use of the fax machine will often be in conjunction with a mobile telephone, and therefore must have connectors to enable them to plug into these as well as into conventional telephone sockets. And there is no need for the fax machine itself to incorporate a telephone. One other aspect to emerge from discussion with potential users is the fax machine could be useful in conjunction with a portable computer, both as a scanner of documents for entering into the computer and as a printer. Appropriate sockets and connectors are therefore also necessary for this.

In fact, it transpires that the concept of a portable fax machine can be rethought as a portable modem-scanner-printer for use in conjunction with a laptop computer and/or mobile telephone. It may be the designers will be able to suggest to the client something that is a new type of product, rather than being just a new product variant.

An outline performance specification for the portability attribute is therefore developed as follows.

Performance specification

Attribute: portability

- can be carried in one hand – preferably has a carrying handle;
- weight not more than 4 kg, including batteries;
- optional carrying case, with pockets for power and connector cables;
- maximum base dimensions – 300 mm x 300 mm;
- operating environment ranges – temperature from 1°C to 35°C; relative humidity from 20 per cent to 70 per cent;
- weatherproof against rain showers when not in use;
- silent in use – no warning/function bleepers, etc.;
- displays and controls legible in low-light environments;
- compatible with fixed and mobile telephones;
- compatible with portable computers;
- power sources – mains, own battery, car cigarette-lighter socket.

(Source: Cross, 2000)

As I mentioned above, about specifying requirements, a design specification creates a strong link between product planning and product evaluation, because the attributes and performance requirements of the design specification are also those that might be used in evaluating a product. Indeed, a major role for the design specification is in checking and evaluating partial design solutions as they develop, and in comparing and choosing between possible alternative proposals for design solutions. The specification is therefore a key document that will influence, guide and control the rest of the product design process. The next stage, of generating ideas for those possible design solutions, is the subject of Block 3.

Summarise key points of the section

Before reading my summary of the key points of this section, make your own summary in your Workfile.

Key points of Section 10

The product design specification is a more precise and specific development from the design brief. Like the brief, it emphasises ends, not means – what the product design has to achieve, but not how to achieve it.

The specification can be developed from analysing the benefits the user might expect to acquire from the product. Such benefit statements need to be converted into more precise statements of user requirements and product performance.

Learning outcomes for Section 10 are 1.4, 2.5, 3.3 and 3.4.

Postscript

Answers to self-assessment questions

SAQ 1

If a deodorant company is 'really in the underarm business', what business would you say the producers of the following products are really in? Think of the needs each product addresses.

(a) Vacuum cleaners.

Cleaning and maintenance.

(b) Computers.

Information and communication technology.

(c) Potato peelers.

Food preparation.

(d) Televisions.

Entertainment and/or information displays.

SAQ 2

From what you may know about them, try to locate the following products, at the time of their first introduction to the market, within the market-pull-technology-push, product-planning matrix (Figure 8).

(a) Dyson cyclone bagless vacuum cleaner.

Product development (bottom-right: new technology in established market).

(b) Sony Walkman audio cassette player.

Product innovation (top-right: new product type, new market).

(c) Sony Walkman CD player.

Product development (top-left: current technology, new market).

(d) IBM personal computer – which established the abbreviation PC.

Product innovation (top-right: new technology, new market).

(e) Any one of a number of low-cost, personal computers launched each year.

Product renewal (bottom-left: current technology, current market).

Your answers might differ from mine. It is not always possible to categorise new products unambiguously into such a simple market-pull-technology-push matrix.

SAQ 3

Thinking back to Section 1.2, what business would you say the producers of kettles are really in?

Kettle producers are in the business of providing hot water for a variety of domestic uses, ranging from food preparation to hot-water bottles, and boiled water for some specific uses such as tea-making and providing safe drinking water such as in preparing baby-feed. But kettle producers usually also produce other related products, and so their business might be seen as electrical kitchen products. A wider view might be to consider the business of hot drinks, since this is a common purpose of heating water in a kettle, and where another potentially relevant innovation has been the introduction of self-heating drinks cans.

SAQ 4

Summarise the procedure for the evolutionary forecasting method.

Look at the origins and the broad historical development of the chosen product type.

Look for major patterns of change over broad time intervals.

Use these patterns and an analysis of the current form and/or features of the product type to forecast future developments.

SAQ 5

Compare the kansei engineering approach with the focus group approach.

Both the kansei engineering and the focus group methods of market research and product development are concerned with gaining insights into how people respond to product designs, and the sorts of benefits they are expecting to gain from products. Their differences are shown below.

Kansei engineering	Focus group
There are two basic approaches: 1 formalised, detailed testing of people's responses to alterations in a product; 2 observations of a product in use, leading to suggestions for improvements or new product features.	Method uses group discussion of users' experiences with and perceptions of a product, and seeks to reveal people's preferences. Discussion group leader may prompt particular attention on to certain product features.

SAQ 6

In what ways do you think that concerns with design for the environment would be reflected in a producer company's commercial strategy for new products?

A producer company would want new products it can demonstrate or advertise as being environment-friendly. The products might have to conform with new voluntary regulation or legislation, and this might be demonstrated, for example, through prominent display of ecolabels or energy labels. A company would consider developments in areas such as:

- energy – reduced energy consumption during product use, for example more efficient motors, lower power rating, or improved insulation; alternative energy sources, for example solar, human (wind-up) power;
- materials – sustainable sources, recycled or at least recyclable materials, reduced or alternative packaging;
- manufacture and distribution – reduced energy consumption, local manufacture and distribution;
- recycling – design for disassembly (identification and easier separation of parts), reusable components;

- emissions – design to reduce toxic emissions and wastes during manufacture, use and disposal;
- product life – more durable products, classic designs that don't date, upgradeable products.

In the extreme, a company might consider its overall business mission, and think in terms of service provision rather than tangible products, and strategies such as product leasing.

SAQ 7

Outline in your own words, in just one or two sentences, the main design principle that Donald Norman illustrates with his examples in the passage above.

The design principle is visibility, which means making clear how a product operates or is used. Inadequate visibility leads to uncertainty, mistakes and rejection of the product; over-complexity (profusion of controls, and so on) leads to confusion and intimidation.

SAQ 8

What causes of variation did Victor Papanek introduce to increase the scope of the user populations he considered?

Papanek 'broadens the constituency' for design by taking into consideration the variations due to size, age and disability, and other factors such as circumstances of use and strength.

SAQ 9

Summarise the three main stages in a user trip as described here.

1 Decide on point(s) of view you will adopt for the user or users.
2 Decide on the limits and the variations to the user trip or trips you are going to take.
3 Carry out the trip or trips, recording your actions, impressions, thoughts and ideas.

SAQ 10

There are two different procedures for carrying out user tests as described here, depending on whether you are using experienced or inexperienced users. Summarise the steps in each approach.

Experienced users

1 Identify and seek the cooperation of relevant users.
2 Prepare some questions, but conduct unstructured interviews with the users, recording their comments, thoughts and ideas.
3 Observe the users actually using the product, and record any critical, difficult or unusual aspects.

Inexperienced users

1 Obtain a volunteer who is inexperienced in using the product, or introduce some novel task or feature into its use.
2 Give the volunteer an objective to be achieved, but no instructions on how to achieve it.

3 Observe the inexperienced user's attempts to achieve the objective; ask them to talk about their difficulties as they experience them, and record both your and their observations and comments.

SAQ 11

Can you think of any potential shortcomings in the use of personas in the process of new product design?

The main dangers would be to fall into the trap of designing for the average user, or consciously or unconsciously to use yourself, or a similar person, as the model for a persona. A persona is meant to represent a real user, not an average one or a familiar person. The dangers can be reduced by developing a range of personas to represent different users of the product.

SAQ 12

Identify the goal, the context, the constraints, and the criteria in the design brief for the domestic computer trolley.

Goal. Design a moveable furniture item to accommodate home computer equipment.

Context. Using computers at home; using for study, business, games, and information searching.

Constraints. Price; timescale for development.

Criteria. Aesthetically satisfactory; space-saving; usable by both adults and children.

SAQ 13

For a user group of teenagers, suggest at least one desired product benefit in each of the four pleasures (as above) for the domestic computer trolley for which a brief was suggested in Section 9.

Here are some suggestions.

Physio-pleasure

- The trolley should be easy to move around.
- The trolley should be robust.
- The surface heights for keyboard, monitor, and so on should be simple to adjust.

Socio-pleasure

- The trolley should facilitate shared or group use, for example for computer games.

Psycho-pleasure

- The trolley should convey the impression of a young, modern computer user.

Ideo-pleasure

- The trolley should look good in a teenager's room.
- The trolley should be user-friendly.
- The trolley should be environment-friendly.

References

Bailey, R.W. (1982) *Human Performance Engineering: A guide for systems designers*, New Jersey, Prentice Hall.

Bernsen, J. (1996) 'The design before the design', *Danish Design Centre Magazine*, no. 2.

Blackler, A., Popovic, V. and Mahar, D. (2003) 'The nature of intuitive use of products', *Design Studies*, vol. 24, no. 6, pp. 491–506.

Buur, J. (1989) *Mechatronics Design in Japan*, Lyngby, Denmark, Technical University of Denmark.

Cagan, J. and Vogel, C. M. (2002) *Creating Breakthrough Products*, New Jersey, Prentice Hall.

Cooper, A. (1999) *The Inmates are Running the Asylum*, Indianapolis, SAMS.

Cross, N. (2000) *Engineering Design Methods*, Chichester, Wiley.

Cross, N. (2001) 'Achieving pleasure from purpose: the methods of Kenneth Grange, product designer', *The Design Journal*, vol. 4, no. 1, pp. 48–58.

Jordan, P. (2000) *Designing Pleasurable Products*, London, Taylor and Francis.

Myerson, J. (2001) *IDEO: Masters of Innovation*, New York, te Neues Publishing Company.

Norman, D. A. (1998) *The Design of Everyday Things*, London, MIT Press.

Oakley, M. (1984) *Managing Product Design*, London, Weidenfeld and Nicolson.

Open University (2001) M873 *User Interface Design and Evaluation*, Unit 2, *Investigations and analyses for UI design*, Milton Keynes, The Open University.

Papanek, V. (1983) *Design for Human Scale*, New York, Van Nostrand Reinhold.

Roy, R. (1990) 'Product design and company performance', in Oakley, M. (ed) *Design Management*, Oxford, Blackwell.

Suchman, L. (1987) *Plans and Situated Actions: The problem of human-machine communication*, Cambridge, Cambridge University Press.

Ulrich, K. T. and Eppinger, S. D. (1995) *Product Design and Development*, New York, McGraw-Hill.

Walsh, V.M., Roy, R., Bruce, M. and Potter, S. (1999) *Winning by Design*, Oxford, Blackwell.

www.designcouncil.info/inclusivedesign/Mattwhite/challenge.html (Accessed April, 2003)

www.hermanmiller.com/hm/content/research_summaries/wp_Anthropometrics.pdf (Accessed April, 2003)

www.pre.nl/ecodesign/ecodesign.htm (Accessed April, 2003)

www.ricability.org.uk (Accessed April, 2003)

www.upmystreet.com (Accessed April, 2003)

Acknowledgements

Grateful acknowledgement is made to the following sources for permission to reproduce material within this book.

Text

Pages 11–13, 38, 39, 90 and 91: *Creating Breakthrough Products: Innovation from product planning to program approval*, Jonathan Cagan and Craig M. Vogel, (2002), Pearson Education. Reproduced by permission of Pearson Education, Inc. Pages 42 and 43: *Ecodesign Tools*, © PRé Consultants, Netherlands, 2000–2003. All rights reserved. Pages 45 and 46: Norman, D. A. (1989) 'The Frustration of Everyday Life', *The Design of Everyday Things*, published by MIT Press, first edition, 1998. Pages 53–55: Papanek, V, (1983), *Design for Human Scale*, Van Nostrand Reinhold Company Inc. Pages 57 and 58: the Design Council. Pages 66, 67, 82, 83, 99, 100–102: Jordan, P.W. (2000) *Designing Pleasurable Products*, Taylor & Francis Books Ltd. Pages 77–79: *Choosing a vacuum cleaner that's easy to use*, www.ricability.org.uk Pages 95– 97: adapted from Bernsen, J. 'The design before the design', *Danish Design Centre Magazine*, no. 2, 1996. Pages 103 and 104: K. Ulrich and S. Eppinger, *Product Design and Development*. Copyright © 1995 by McGraw-Hill Companies, Inc. All rights reserved. Pages 105 and 106: *Engineering Design Methods: Strategies for product design*, Cross, N. © 2000 by John Wiley & Sons Ltd. Reproduced by permission of John Wiley & Sons Limited.

Photographs and illustrations

Figure 4: Oxo Good Grips. Figures 6 and 7: Sony UK. Figures 9 and 10: courtesy of Kenneth Grange. Figure 11(a and b): Science and Society Picture Library; Figure 11(e): Saitek. Figure 12: Oakely, M. (1984) *Managing Production*, Wiedenfeld & Nicolson. Figure 15: Mary Evans Picture Library. Figure 16: Ford Motor Company. Figure 17: Mazda Motors UK Limited. Figure 18: Buur, J. (1989) *Mechatronics Design in Japan*, Denmark, Technical University of Denmark. Figure 19(c): Philips Consumer Electronics. Figure 25: Diffrient, N., Tilley, A. R. and Bardagjy, J. C. (1974), *Humanscale 1/2/3: A portfolio of information*, MIT Press. Figure 29: Herman Miller Inc. Figure 30: Japan Hobby and Gift. Figure 34: Helen Hamlyn Research Centre and B&Q. Figures 38 and 48: courtesy of IDEO. Figure 49: IDEO. Figure 50: images taken from *Smart Design* by Clive Grinyer, published by RotoVision, November, 2001, www.rotovision.com

Every effort has been made to trace all copyright owners. If any have been inadvertently overlooked, the publishers will be pleased to make the necessary arrangements at the first opportunity.

Course Team

Academic staff

Ken Baynes, External Assessor
Catherine Cooke, Author
Nigel Cross, Author
Chris Earl, Author
Steve Garner, Author and Course Chair
Georgy Holden, Author
Robin Roy, Author

Consultants

Mark Evans, Contributing Author, Workbook 1

Associate lecturers

Jenny Burke
Nick Jeffrey

Course managers

Andy Harding, Course Manager
Amber Thomas, Course Manager

Production staff

Tammy Alexander, Graphic Designer
Margaret Barnes, Course Secretary
Philippa Broadbent, Print Buyer
Jane Bromley, Interactive Media Designer
Michael Brown, Video Editor
Daphne Cross, Assistant Print Buyer
Tony Duggan, Learning Projects Manager
Bernie D'Souza, Course Secretary
Barbara Fraser, Picture Researcher
Phil Gauron, Video Producer
Richard Hearne, Photographer
Katie Meade, Rights Executive
Jane Moore, Editor
Jonathon Owen, Graphic Artist
Alex Reid, Narrator (video)
Ekkehard Thumm, Media Project Manager
Howie Twiner, Graphic Artist
Robert Wood, Editor